GEORGE EDWARDS

The Bedell and his Birds

by
A. Stuart Mason
MD FRCP

ROYAL COLLEGE OF PHYSICIANS

Royal College of Physicians of London
11 St Andrews Place, London NW1 4LE
Registered Charity No. 210508

Copyright © 1992 Royal College of Physicians of London
ISBN 1 873240 48 1

Printed in Great Britain by The Lavenham Press Ltd,
Lavenham, Sudbury, Suffolk

Peint par Dandridge.

Gravé par Ambroise Tardieu.

GEORGE EDWARDS

(Zoologiste.)

Membre de la Société royale de Londres.

Né à West Ham (Comté d'Essex) le 3 Avril 1693.

Mort à Plaistow le 23 Juillet 1773.

George Edwards, bedell of the College of Physicians 1733–1760. Engraved from a portrait painted in 1754 by Bartholomew Dandridge.

Acknowledgements

I am indebted to many people for advice and encouragement in pleasurable discussion of Edwards' life and work. I am especially grateful to Sir Cyril Clarke for writing the Foreword that graces this book. I am also very grateful to the Harveian Librarian, Sir Christopher Booth for his encouragement, to Mr Geoffrey Davenport and his staff in the library of the Royal College of Physicians, and to Mrs Gina Douglas, librarian of the Linnaean Society. I owe a particular debt of thanks to Mrs Christine Jackson, author of *Bird Etchings*, for her expert advice and continued interest, and to Mr William Drummond for his expert opinion on Edwards as an artist. Thanks to Mr C. J. Holyoake, the heraldic significance of Edwards' bookplate was revealed. Finally, I am most grateful to Miss Diana Beaven of the College publications department for her perceptive editing and for her hard work in transforming the text into an illustrated book, and to Mrs Suzanne Fuzzey for her advice on design.

A. STUART MASON

Contents

List of illustrations

FOREWORD

Oh, to have been around in the 1730s – for then a third of the Fellows of the Royal College of Physicians were also Fellows of the Royal Society, all 'curious men' and interested in natural history, identifying and classifying not only diseases, but monkeys, birds, fish, butterflies and flowers – and indeed anything living. They wrote up their research discoveries in easily comprehensible English, and often in French as well, despite the little matter of our being at war with France. The more stuffy two-thirds of the College of Physicians looked down their noses at the upstart Royal Society, with its socially mixed classes.

Our hero is George Edwards who, after miscellaneous studies as a young man, attracted the attention of Hans Sloane, President of both learned bodies, who, with others, had spotted Edwards' artistic talents, and in 1733 Edwards became the bedell of the Royal College of Physicians, converting his quarters there into a studio (a phenomenon not seen since) where he worked on his drawings and etchings, principally of birds.

Edwards thrived because the 'curious men' needed accurate drawings of their collections and he became a superb recorder, so much so that in 1744 he was offered the Fellowship of the Royal Society, but he declined this initially as he felt he had not contributed enough. As might be guessed from this, he was a bachelor and to some extent a loner, but not without his tender side. Thus, a French ship, captured by Captain Shirley Washington RN (later Earl Ferrers FRS) had in it a 'parcel of natural objects' which included birds that had been destined for Madame de Pompadour. George was asked to draw them. Sorry that any beautiful lady should be disappointed, he named one of the birds Pompadour: 'it being a bird of excessive beauty, I hope the lady will forgive me for calling it by her name'. We have seen the painting, and the tears came to our eyes as we looked at it in *Gleanings of Natural History*, now safely housed in the library of his beloved College of Physicians (where it was published in 1764), and it is also in the Linnaean Society.

Edwards' observations on the aggressiveness of bantam cocks shut up without hens led him to condemn the segregation of the sexes in schools 'just when their natural affections were blossoming' and so 'acts unnatural were introduced in place of the natural'. In the 1990s he is immediately dubbed a homosexual – and he may well have had streaks of it like most of us – but I prefer to think of him as just having a complicated, manic-depressive temperament with all its advantages.

Edwards was finally elected FRS in 1757 when he had given ten formal presentations, four of them being published in the *Philosophical Transactions*. A study of his work gives us not only a slice of the social background but also an insight into the intellectual life of the 18th century, when a variety of people were enthusiastically trying to make logical sense of natural history, and the classification of species was an essential base for later work.

For the Royal College of Physicians, Edwards, though never a Fellow, was better known than most of the Presidents of his day, and in addition to running the library he designed and etched the plates for the various printed summonses to the College, all decorated with the College coat of arms, to which he added his own thought: 'Ars longa, vita brevis'. He also arranged the Croonian sermons, which still survive.

References, though essential, are usually boring, but here they are spiced with notes and quotations which again show the spirit of the age, thus increasing the nostalgia engendered by the whole book.

SIR CYRIL CLARKE FRS FRCP
President, Royal College of Physicians, 1972-77

The small etchings reproduced at the beginning and end of each chapter are taken from *Gleanings of Natural History* and are by George Edwards.

INTRODUCTION

The New Philosophy, based on enquiry into nature by experiment and observation, was developed during the Commonwealth and, after the Restoration, inspired the foundation of the Royal Society in 1663[1]. The Society brought together an odd amalgam of noblemen, physicians, writers and antiquarians, whose common tie was an interest in new knowledge. Until this time, the City of London had considered the College of Physicians to be the one learned society. However, physicians, particularly Sir George Ent and Dr Christopher Merrett, a good naturalist and keeper of the College library and museum, played an active part in the founding of the Royal Society, welcoming a wider participation in the study of nature.

The Royal Society became the intellectual centre for experimentalists and collectors, all of whom were enthusiasts but not specialists; to be interested in only one subject was unthinkable. After all, Christopher Wren, a founding fellow of the Society, was a professor of astronomy before he designed St Paul's Cathedral. Most of the collectors collected for the fun of it, each man trying to form his own museum, artefacts vying with natural objects. The popularity of these activities grew and attracted much criticism, some of it deserved. Dr Baldwin Hamey Jnr, the greatest benefactor of the College of Physicians, was so incensed at the progress of a learned society that was not the College that he paid the Reverend Stubbs, an erudite but acrimonious pamphleteer, to attack the Royal Society[2]. Stubbs accused it of fostering atheism and also of harbouring Papists. Thomas Shadwell satirised the Society on stage with his play, *The Virtuoso*, creating the character of Sir Nicholas Gimcrack who indulged in absurd experiments.

However, the New Philosophy and the Royal Society survived the attacks, and the political upheavals in England. The College of Physicians lost its building and library in the Great Fire but gained a magnificent new home in Warwick Lane, uncomfortably close to Newdigate prison. The gift of the Marquess of Dorchester's library more than compensated for the loss of Merrett's books. By the time Queen Anne was on the throne the Royal Society and College of Physicians had settled down. The Society had Isaac Newton as president with Dr (later Sir) Hans Sloane as secretary, a formidable combination of talent. Sloane was the leading physician, becoming president of the College of

Physicians in 1719 and succeeding Newton as president of the Royal Society. He knew everyone who mattered, was an expert natural historian and the foremost of all collectors. His collection of manuscripts was as important as his huge collection of natural objects. The study of collections for the classification of species was an essential part of the advance of natural history in the 18th century. Again, it had its critics. Joseph Addison, in the *Tatler* and the *Spectator*, lampooned Sloane and other collectors by recreating Sir Nicholas Gimcrack and listing his fictional and absurd collection, thus giving the dictionary the word 'gimcrack' for a worthless object.

Nevertheless, the serious work of collectors thrived and they joined with the experimentalists in being known as 'curious men', a complimentary term. Collections needed recording in pictures, which could be sent to fellow enthusiasts; if a collector could not get some specimen he at least needed a picture of it. So there was a demand for artists who could accurately portray all sorts of natural objects. Such an artist was George Edwards, whose skill lay in accurate representation rather than in artistic impression. He, too, was a curious person, a descriptive naturalist who today would probably have been happier with a camera than a paint-brush.

EDWARDS' EARLY LIFE

George Edwards was born in 1694, the only son of fairly well-to-do parents living in West Ham, then a country place where Dr Fothergill later created his great botanical garden at Upton Park. That Edwards was Welsh and proud of it can be deduced from the bookplate he designed for himself which displayed the arms and Welsh motto 'a vinno Duw dervid' (God's will be done) attributed to Tudwr Trefor, founder of a Welsh noble family. These arms were born legitimately by the Edwards family of Lea in Shropshire; George, however, was not a close relative[3].

From a boarding school in Leytonstone, George went on to Brentwood Grammar School where the Reverend Ashpool was headmaster[4]. To fit him for a 'trading life' he took a course in accounting before learning business with John Dod, a tradesman or merchant in Fenchurch Street. Dod was a kindly employer, giving his apprentice the freedom of his considerable library that he had inherited from a physician relative. There, Edwards spent 'all the leisure of the day and not infrequently a considerable part of the night' in reading, particularly the books on natural history. But business did not interest him and he left the long-suffering Mr Dod in 1716.

With his head full of a 'confused mixture' of knowledge, Edwards decided to travel. 'It was,' he said, 'mere curiosity that led me abroad' which is 'commonly termed no business at all'. After a few summer weeks in Holland, he was back in West Ham to spend the next two years in self-confessed idleness. In May 1718 he went to Norway on a ship captained by a friend. Wandering in Scandinavia he heard the guns at Frederickstadt where the Swedes fought the Danes. Edwards was promptly arrested by the Danes as a Swedish spy, but talked his way to freedom.

He returned from Scandinavia to Bristol, stopping off to see the flora and fauna of the Scilly Isles. Making a leisurely journey home, he tasted the fashions of Bath and looked at Blenheim Palace. The next year he was off again, this time to France where he lodged with a schoolmaster in the park of Versailles. From there he did a lot of solitary walking, to Chalons, to Champagne and to Orleans. On this last walk he dressed as a vagrant to avoid the attention of robbers. As a vagrant he was arrested, because 'there had lately been an order from Court to take up all strolling persons who could give no account of themselves in order to

3

transport them to people the banks of the Mississippi.' Again, he talked his way out.

Edwards came back to England in January 1721, '...having been about 21 months from home where I escaped sinking in the South Sea.' Dependent as he was on family money, he must have been more than relieved that his own capital did not disappear when the South Sea Bubble burst in 1720. He may have received his capital when he came of age but it is more likely that it was inherited on the early death of his father for he wrote in 1733 of his patrimony. He had a half-brother, James Frost, so his mother must have been widowed and married again. His frugal journeys were nothing like the fashionable Grand Tour of the rich, but were all that he could afford. They satisfied his desire to travel and enabled him to become fluent in French.

Edwards himself recorded his travels, but his life in West Ham was noted by his friend and later biographer, James Robson, a New Bond Street bookseller. In West Ham, Edwards 'closely pursued his favourite study of natural history; applying himself to drawing and colouring such animals as fell under his notice. A strict attention to natural more than picturesque beauty claimed his earliest care. Birds first engaged his particular attention.'[5] Surrounded as it was by grazing fields and just south of the great Essex forest, West Ham provided an abundance of local fauna. However, Edwards' prime interest was in foreign species and it was West Ham's proximity to the Port of London that mattered to him. The place was home to many sea captains, notably of the Pelley family, from whom foreign birds could be obtained. Over the years Edwards made his own collection from a worldwide network of corre-spondents. Dr Fothergill got his rare plants in the same way for his West Ham garden.

Averse to business and contented with his lot, Edwards reached his thir-ties without bothering to earn an income; teaching young ladies and gentlemen to draw was scarcely gainful employment. However, he was accumulating a considerable portfolio of pictures. These came to the attention of James Theobald FRS, of Lambeth, who introduced him to the world of collectors centred on the Royal Society. To Edwards' sur-prise these curious men proved willing to pay good money for his work. He was quick to exploit this novel situation: 'by the increase of my friends and better encouragement I mended my hand and enlarged my prices.' He may have disliked business but was a good business man. Needing a yardstick for his own work, he went to Holland in 1731 to buy the best published illustrations of natural history. Thanks to

4

Theobald, a man 'zealous for science', he had stumbled into a career and also found a man to guide it.

His guide and chief patron was Sir Hans Sloane who then bestrode the world of science as president of the Royal Society, where he had seen Edwards' work, and of the College of Physicians. Edwards later explained that Sloane 'employed me for a great number of years in drawing miniature figures of animals etc after nature in water colours to increase his very great collection of fine drawings by other hands.'[6] Edwards drew whatever Sloane asked of him, as expected of a recording artist. He figured fish, reptiles, quadrupeds and especially birds. All these pictures by Edwards are now in the Sloane collection in the Manuscript Department of the British Library and the Print Department of the British Museum.[7] Few of the pictures are dated: of those that bear a date, the earliest is 1732 and most are 1740 to 1742. Many are pictures of specimens owned by people other than Sloane. So Edwards got paid by the owner and by Sloane; by supplying copies of his pictures to all interested parties, Edwards increased his income.

5

Custom House and the Port of London through which many of Edwards' specimens were imported. Engraved circa 1750. (Courtesy of the Guildhall Library, London.)

As a draughtsman Edwards' sole aim was to 'achieve a natural and accurate portrayal.' This was not easy when portraying stuffed birds, which he often had to do. He would make at least four drawings of each specimen using 'as many turns and attitudes as I could invent'[8] to achieve a life-like picture. He worked in pen and water-colour but sometimes made preliminary drawings in pencil to note proportion and size. The library of the Zoological Society has a collection of bird sketches in pencil by Edwards; these show little artistic talent.

Troubled by his ignorance of a bird's habitat, which meant that he could not portray it in its natural surroundings, Edwards took 'counsel of some painters my particular friends to decorate the birds with airy grounds.'[9] A lichen-covered bough was his favourite device on which to perch smaller birds. Water fowl he depicted by water. A sketched hint of vegetation and romantic buildings was the general theme of the backgrounds. The most striking composition in the Sloane collection shows an Indian bird on a bough with an eastern palace by a still sea on which a British ship is anchored. Alas, this was a copy of an Indian painting and not the product of Edwards' imagination. He was a painstaking recorder of nature, not a gifted artist, which was just as he saw himself.

Nevertheless, Edwards' bird pictures are beautiful because the beauty of the subjects is so lovingly and faithfully depicted. What is more, Edwards did paint, presumably when commissioned, pictures to delight the eye, rather than instruct. A very attractive composition of birds and butterflies set against a background of detailed romantic landscape is signed and dated 'Edwards, 1732.' Two other pictures, of birds, monkeys etc., were painted in the same style and probably about the same date, although neither is signed or dated. The date of 1732 is significant as after that time Edwards became completely involved with recording birds in pictures and becoming a serious ornithologist. He does not appear to have reverted to the decorative picture later in his career.

Edwards claimed to have invented two methods of representation. He displayed winged insects by painting the body and legs, then gumming the actual wings into place. 'To fulfil a promise to some particular ladies' he described his method of showing the profile of a bird by plucking each feather and gumming them in sequence on to a paper-covered board.[10]

ITINERA VARIA AUCTORIS
From *A Natural History of Birds,* Part 2

To indicate the 'various journeys of the author', Edwards drew this map. He showed by dotted lines, each with a date, the routes of his short voyages. Above the map Edwards illustrates 'the bill of the Ibis of its natural bigness, as it was taken out of an embalmed subject (brought from Egypt) in the presence of his Grace the Duke of Richmond'. The two beetles were brought from the East Indies for the collection of Dr Mathew Lee FRCP. Edwards depicted them as life-size: 'I suppose the uppermost to be the male and the lower the female'.

The inset depicts the Least Humming Bird and its egg; both specimens were brought from Jamaica.

SVECIÆ PARS

NORVEGIA

Christiana

Friederichstad

Christiansand

Maio 1718

Alborg

Wyborg

Billum

Copenha gen

Slejwick

Lubeck

Hamburg

Bremen

Groningen

GERMANIA

OCEANUS

W E
S

Junij 1718

Julio 1718

GERMANICUS

Zuell

Hollandia

Amsterdam

Haag

Aug 1716

Maio 1718 Sep 1715

Julio 1730

Rotterdam

Antwerp

Cologne

Juliers

Liege

FLANDRIA

Dunkirk

Calais

Bologne

Namur

Abbeville

Diepe

Rouen

Remes

Chalons

Paris

Skie I

Inverness

SCOTIA

Aberdean

Dumblain

Montrose

St Andrew

Glacow

Edinburg

Berwick

Cotterton

Glenluce

Dumfries

Ardnamur

Carlisle

Newcastle

Mare

Lancaster

York

Hull

Hibernicum

Liverpool

Lincoln

Dublin

Chester

Darby

Carnarvon

Shrewsbury

Coventry

Norwich

Wexford

ANGLIA

Peterboro

Ipswich

St Davids

Hereford

Worcester

Oxford

Harwich

Bristol

London

Bath

Canterbury

Dover

Exeter

Salisbury

Southampton

Chichester

Julie 1718

OCEANUS BRITANICUS

Guernsey

Jersey

Caen

Brest

Auranche

Versailles

Fontainbleu

Rennes

Le Mans

Orleans

Blois

FRANCIA

Scala per Pedicum sive Domitii Pedes Anglicana.

THE ROYAL COLLEGE OF PHYSICIANS

When the bedell (or beadle)[11] of the Royal College of Physicians died in 1733, Sloane saw an opportunity to advance Edwards and give him another career. Usually the bedell was appointed on the nod of the president. This time, for no known reason, Edwards was faced by eleven candidates for the job. At a meeting of the fellows nine were eliminated and a ballot was held to decide between Edwards and one other. The votes were tied and it needed Sloane's casting vote as president to get Edwards appointed. Sloane had expected to get his way more easily. The opposition did not appear to be against Edwards, who proved to be a popular bedell, but was more likely a reminder to Sloane that the president had to be backed by the will of the fellows.

The bedell was custodian of the College property, including the library, and administrator for a somewhat lethargic organisation. It was a good job, for with it came a rent-free house of considerable size in the College's large building in Warwick Lane near St Paul's. Edwards found the house 'very convenient', as indeed it was, giving him a base in the City not far from the Royal Society in Crane Court, Fleet Street. The official salary of the bedell was £12 a year, topped up by gratuities of £22. For this Edwards was most grateful to Sloane, who by 'adding something to a small patrimony...rendered my condition both easy and happy.'[12] Among the 50 or so fellows of the College, Edwards said he gained: 'as many patrons as there are gentlemen of that learned body.' This was an exaggeration, but about a third of the fellows were also fellows of the Royal Society which was the centre for his career as a naturalist. Moreover, compared with the College, the Society had a broader social spectrum, from dukes to technicians, covering its 300 fellows. Curious physicians looked to the Society, not to the College, for their intellectual stimulation.

Edwards always described himself as keeper of the library of the College of Physicians, although officially there was no such post. As bedell it was one of his duties to care for the library. There was indeed a major collection of about 8000 books, thanks to the gift of Lord Dorchester's magnificent library which replaced the original library destroyed in 1666 by the Great Fire of London.[13] Although the responsibilities of the College's bedell were wide, the workload was light enough for Edwards to continue his career as a naturalist, which must have taken him away from the College on many occasions.

Hans Sloane, President of the College of Physicians, 1719–1735. Born in Ireland in 1660, Sloane came to London in 1679 and was befriended by Robert Boyle and John Ray, two leading scientists. He then studied medicine and botany in Paris and Montpellier, taking his MD at the University of Orange in 1683. Returning to London he lived with and was taught by Dr Sydenham. Elected FRS in 1685, he became FRCP in 1687 and went to Jamaica with the Duke of Albemarle; he later wrote his classic book on the natural history of that island. He was appointed Secretary of the Royal Society in 1693 and two years later married the wealthy widow of Fulk Rose. Settling in Bloomsbury and, in 1712, making the shrewd purchase of the manor of Chelsea, he built up a royal and aristocratic practice, yet never refused a patient who could not pay. He was created a baronet in 1716 and elected President of the College of Physicians in 1719, serving until 1735. In 1727 he became President of the Royal Society, retiring from the office in 1741. His long retirement in Chelsea was devoted to his huge collections. He was a great and generous facilitator of science throughout the world. Sloane died in 1753, leaving his collections to the nation for the foundation of the British Museum.

After five years of this busy organised life, Edwards considered publishing a book on birds, based on his growing number of pictures. There was a scarcity of well illustrated books on birds in English. The most authoritative was Willughby's *Ornithologia* published in 1676; this was a comprehensive study of English and foreign birds but even Willughby had complained of the poor standard of the engraved illustrations. The book was one of a series on natural history written by Willughby and John Ray. Willughby died young and much of his work was edited by Ray, the son of a Braintree blacksmith, who became a distinguished botanist, a close friend of Sloane's, and inspired Mark Catesby, also an Essex man, to take up natural history. Edwards used Willughby's book all his life, annotating the text and referring to it in his drawings. He had a mind to publish a revised edition, but never completed the task.

Attractive but lifeless engravings of birds were made by Eleazar Albin and published, thanks to the financial help of Dr Richard Mead, from 1731 to 1736 to form one book. Albin was an artist and teacher of painting, not a naturalist. Edwards was rightly critical of Albin's accuracy and proudly noted that one of his patrons 'was not well satisfied with the draughts Albin made.'[14]

Edwards concentrated on painting foreign birds and his nearest rival was his good friend Mark Catesby, who pictured many American birds in his folio book on the natural history of Carolina, where he had worked for years as a naturalist. Catesby was living in Hoxton, London, when he published his book, in parts, from 1731 to 1743. All the illustrations were etchings made by Catesby, who had been taught to etch by Joseph Groupy, a French born artist who worked in London.

The physicians encouraged Edwards to publish, probably by promising individual subscriptions for his book, as was the custom of the time. But he was put off by 'the great expense of graving, printing and other things which I knew would be a certain cost with a very uncertain profit.'[15] Perhaps he was aware of the financial struggles of Catesby, although it was Catesby who came to the rescue by offering to teach Edwards the art of etching. Learning to engrave copperplates was a more time-consuming process than learning to etch, and Edwards was in a hurry to learn a technique that he could use to illustrate his book.

The first etching that he thought good enough to show to others was of a mountain finch, dated 1739: 'Edwards' first tryal at etching', wrote Henry Seymer, a Dorset client of Edwards, on his copy.[16] The reversed image of the last two digits of the date on the print shows that Edwards was not yet practised in etching titles in mirror-writing to produce a leg-

The College of Physicians' building in Warwick Lane, viewed from the entrance archway. The entrance to the bedell's house is the second door on the left. Drawn and engraved by David Logan, 1677.

COLLEGIUM REGALE MEDICORUM LONDINENSIUM

ible print. In the same year he put his newly acquired skill to the service of the College, etching a summons to Comitia (the quarterly meeting of fellows), embellished with the Arms of the College.

Edwards based his etchings on his large collection of watercolours. He soon realised that a black and white etched print that had to be hand-coloured was not a replica of a watercolour. So he set about composing his etchings as original pictures. 'It often happens', he wrote years later, 'that my figures on copperplate differ from my original drawings, for sometimes the originals have not altogether pleased me as to their attitudes and actions.' So he chose from his four or more pictures of one subject the 'one that I judged most free and natural to be engraved on my plate.'[17] In his later career Edwards became so confident of his etching skills that he often drew from nature directly on to the waxed copperplate without making preliminary sketches. He was convinced that a recording artist must make his own etchings or engravings and not follow the usual custom of handing over pictures to be copied by an engraver, for: 'it cannot be supposed that the hired operators had opportunity ... to study the ... attitudes of the subjects while living.'[18] The composition of Edwards' etchings often included more than one specimen, usually combining birds and insects, as he objected to 'too great void spaces on the copperplate.'[19]

13

The Mountain Finch. This uncoloured etching by Edwards, made in 1739, was the first to be shown to the public. Edwards gave this copy to Henry Seymer of Dorchester who later inserted it, with other uncoloured etchings by Edwards, into his copy of Gleanings of Natural History. *(By permission of the Linnaen Society of London.)*

the great pied ... ... Finch or Bramlin . 1788

The hand colouring of an etching, particularly of a bird, is crucial to accurate portrayal. Thus Edwards himself coloured at least a dozen copies of all the etchings he published in his book and personally supervised the colouring of others. He deposited in the College of Physicians one complete set of etchings 'carefully and exactly coloured from the original drawings which may serve as a standard to refer to...in case the Plates should outlive me.'[15] Mindful that 'colouring work in London, when highly finished comes very dear', Edwards used a restricted palette. It was essential for him to cut costs and so it is unlikely that he ever kept more sets of coloured prints than there were paid-up subscribers to his book. Hired colourists of later sets would have used his reference set to guide their work.[20]

Edwards was in the habit of giving to fellows of the Royal Society his uncoloured prints so that they had the amusement of colouring them; the gift also advertised the forthcoming book. Whether or not he sold individual prints through the many print shops then available is not known. However, for many of his etchings he followed the practice of map and print makers of obtaining copyright protection under the 1735 Act of Parliament which laid down that the maker's name, date of publication and reference to the Act had to be engraved upon the plate. Of the 100 etchings that Edwards made for his book, 37 had this formula engraved, with the date of publication being before the publication of the etchings in book form.[21]

The amount of single-handed labour that Edwards put in to the production of his illustrations for the book was remarkable. He turned his house within the College of Physicians into a studio and workshop where he etched his copperplates, made his drawings and finally printed from his etched plates. The College had never seen this type of activity and never saw it again once Edwards had gone.

Edwards wrote the text for all his books, describing the illustrations some time after the etchings had been made. This is more obvious in later volumes. For instance, etchings titled 'Small Birds from Surinam' have the individual birds named in the accompanying text. Another example is the text that reads: 'The beetle is called the Rhinoceras beetle tho' by mistake the Elephant is wrote on the plate.' Additional text consisted of prefaces for the two volumes and, for the second volume, notes on birds of passage, watercolouring and etching, together with an account of Edwards' early life. The story of his youthful travels was enhanced by a map of Europe decorated with a beetle, humming bird and long beak of a mummified Egyptian ibis. The map is a delightful cartographic curiosity, as Edwards said, 'an uncommon mixture of a geographical chart and the figures of natural history.'

THE PEACOCK PHEASANT FROM CHINA
From *A Natural History of Birds*, Part 2

After a typically detailed description of the plumage, Edward writes: 'Tho' it be a grave coloured bird, yet it is one of the greatest beauties of nature; one may compare it to Sable, thick set with shining jewels of various colours . . . This bird when I drew it was the property of James Monro, MD of London, a most obliging gentleman . . . It has since been presented to Lord Orford and is now living in his house in the Exchequer'.

Of the flowers, Edwards writes: 'The flower, here figured by way of decoration, is called the Chinese Rose: I drew it from Nature'. 'This beautiful flowering tree was raised by the late curious and Noble Lord Petre in his stoves at Thorndon Hall, Essex'.

17

THE BOOK PUBLISHED

Edwards' declared aim was to publish a book with 100 illustrations, split into two volumes. The first volume was published in 1743, entitled *A Natural History of Birds, most of which have not been Figured or Described*. It was, like subsequent volumes, a collection of foreign rarities, for these had been the objects of all his studies. Later, he justified the lack of English birds on the grounds that he did not wish to portray 'any English birds already figured'.[22] The title page stated that the book was 'printed for the author at the College of Physicians in Warwick Lane'. The unnamed printer was very probably his friend Bowyer of Leytonstone, printer to the Society of Antiquaries and later to the College of Physicians.

As Edwards had used the College as a publishing house, he rightly dedicated the first volume to The President and Fellows of the Royal College of Physicians. By then Sir Hans Sloane had given up the presidency of the College and of the Royal Society: the quiet Dr Henry Plumptre had become president of the College, and Martin Folkes president of the Royal Society.

The second volume, with the same title page as the first, was not published until 1747. There was a good reason for the delay; Edwards had not prepared all the material for the book by the time that he published the first volume. This made good commercial sense; if the first volume did not sell, Edwards could cut his losses by abandoning the project. On the other hand, good sales of the first volume would provide the money to finance production of the second volume and would attract more subscribers for the completed work. Illustrated books on natural history were expensive to produce and Edwards was following the cautious example of Albin and Catesby in publishing in parts; he did not have the private sponsorship enjoyed by these two authors.

The second volume was dedicated to Sir Hans Sloane, then confined by age to his manor of Chelsea. When the book appeared, Peter Collinson, City merchant and botanist, wrote to the Swedish naturalist Carl Linnaeus: 'Catesby's noble work is finished. I drank tea a few days ago with Sir Hans Sloane, and he continues to admiration in good spirits and hearty. We often talk of you. Mr Edwards has lately published two very curious volumes in 4to of rare and non-descript birds and animals, all coloured after the life.'[23] This was good news for Linnaeus of Uppsala

Charles Lennox, second Duke of Richmond, was one of Edwards' chief patrons. Born in 1701, he married Sarah, daughter of William, first Earl Cadogan, 1719. He succeeded to his title in 1723, having served as Member of Parliament for Chichester in the previous year. On the death of his grandmother, the Duchess of Portsmouth (Louise de Keroualle) he succeeded to the Dukedom of Aubigny, France. Having been ADC to George I and George II, he became Master of the Horse and a Privy Councillor in 1735. A man of many enthusiasms and a discerning patron, the Duke of Richmond improved his family seat at Goodwood and maintained a fine house in Whitehall, overlooking the Thames. His marriage to Sarah proved to be an enduring love match, although their betrothal was alleged to have been arranged by their parents in settlement of a gambling debt. He died in 1750.

University, who led the field in the classification of plants and animals. It was the beginning of a long friendship between Edwards and Linnaeus, his admirer.

Edwards took the bold step for a first-time author of preparing a French edition of his book, also published from the College at Warwick Lane. He was no doubt encouraged by the example of Catesby, whose text was in French and English, and supported by the Royal Society's close links with French scientists, forged by Sloane. The text was 'traduit de l'Anglais par MD de la SR'. This disguised the translator, Monsieur Durand FRS, a French protestant minister serving the French church in

London and engaged in much translation work. The first French volume was published in 1745, dedicated to Charles Lennox, second Duke of Richmond. The second, published in 1748, was dedicated to the Duchess of Richmond. The Duke got a eulogy of his accomplishments, particularly of his knowledge of French and natural history, with a compliment on his menagerie at Goodwood.[24] Edwards counted the Duke as one of his chief patrons, probably because of his introductions rather than his commissions. Richmond was an enthusiastic patron of many, from cricketers to Canaletto. He was a great collector, an active fellow of the Royal Society, and also an inactive fellow of the Royal College of Physicians.[25]

Edwards' first volume of *A Natural History of Birds*, published in 1743, was an immediate success. It was so highly thought of at the Royal Society that in April 1744 ten fellows proposed Edwards for election to the fellowship as 'a gentleman well acquainted with natural history' who had 'lately obliged the curious...in a book'.[26] The proposers included the Society's president, secretary and past president (Martin Folkes, Dr Cromwell Mortimer and Sir Hans Sloane), Catesby, the ever faithful Theobald, Collinson, and his friend Henry Baker who invented a system for teaching the deaf. Cromwell Mortimer FRCP practised in Bloomsbury in order that he could help Sloane with his patients and his collection, and he continued to work there after Sloane retired.

There could not have been a more distinguished group of proposers. Yet Edwards, who had signified his desire to be a fellow, sent word within a fortnight that he wished the proposal to be withdrawn. His rejection of a coveted honour was extraordinary and difficult to explain. Possibly this was an example of the diffidence and humility noted by his biographer and friend, Robson. Or perhaps he felt that the bedell, a servant of the College of Physicians, should not accept such an honour. He was unlikely to have been put off by the modest outlay of £2 for election and £2.12.0. for an annual subscription. The real answer lay deep in his personality.

Edwards continued to use the Royal Society as his intellectual centre and within a month of withdrawing the proposal for fellowship he made his first formal presentation there. He exhibited a preserved bird of 'the Owl kind which is designed for the museum of the Society' and distributed among the fellows 25 uncoloured prints of his etching portraying the bird, reminding them that the coloured print would appear in the second volume of his book. In describing[27] this great white owl from Hudson's Bay he noted that pictures of it were owned by Sloane and Collinson, the latter's picture being drawn from life. Yet Edwards

T O

G   O   D,

The O N E Eternal! the Incomprehenſible! the
Omnipreſent! Omniſcient, and Almighty CREATOR
of all Things that exiſt! from Orbs immenſurably great,
to the minuteſt Points of Matter, this A T O M is Dedicated and Devoted, with all poſſible Gratitude, Humili-
ation, Worſhip,   and the higheſt Adoration both of
Body and Mind,

By

His moſt reſigned,

Low, and humble Creature,

George Edwards.

added: 'I cannot discover that this bird has been so much as named by
any natural historian or voyager.' The implication that no bird could be
called 'described' until described by Edwards crops up elsewhere in his
work; he was not diffident in his claims, although he did acknowledge
work published by others.

As Edwards had pictures of some 500 birds in his portfolio and the first
two volumes of his book had proved popular, he decided to extend the
book with two further volumes, published in 1750 and 1751. The third
volume was dedicated, once again, to the president and fellows of the
College of Physicians, which he still used as his publishing house. The
fourth volume was dedicated, simply and humbly, to God. The French
volumes were both published in 1751, one dedicated to Folkes, the other

to Dr Richard Mead, both of whom were considered by Edwards to be among his four main supporters.

Martin Folkes inherited a fortune but was no scientist or collector; he simply liked to preside over societies, both the Royal Society and the Society of Antiquaries, to which he got Edwards elected in 1752. Edwards had trouble in finding a suitable dedicatory compliment so settled on praising Folkes for making the Grand Tour after his marriage, when his judgement was mature. The cantankerous Dr Stukeley FRCP had another story.[28] According to him, Folkes' marriage to the actress Mrs Bracegirdle so grieved his mother that she threw herself from a window but escaped serious injury. The Grand Tour was also a disaster for, when in Rome, the new Mrs Folkes went religiously mad. As Folkes had taken with him his pet dog, parrot and monkey, things were not easy for her.

It was easy to compliment the charismatic Dr Mead for he was the cynosure of all in medicine and natural science. As an exemplar of physicianly virtues he was elected president of the College of Physicians but refused to accept the office. The fortune he made from a fashionable practice he spent on his library and on his collections which included a considerable number of items related to natural science. He also paid for the publication of Albin's book on birds. For Edwards he provided a family of patrons; himself, his brother and son, and two daughters, both of whom married Royal physicians.

The publication of the fourth volume of *Birds* marked the end of the book. Edwards completed it with a new title page to be bound in the front of his first volume.[29] The new and final title was *A Natural History of Uncommon Birds.* To go with this he etched a frontispiece with an elaborate classical picture that framed the words 'Ornithologia Nova', a direct reference to Willughby's *Ornithologia.*

The effort of extending the book into four volumes, with English and French editions, must have been immense. Edwards was exhausted by it. In the third volume he wrote that 'declining age...and growing incapacities are reasons for me to discontinue proceeding in this work, that by laying too heavy on the brain may only serve to stupify myself without being of benefit or advantage to the world'.[30] These are the sentiments of a depressive personality and not those of a successful author ending his work.

Edwards further emphasised his failings in his title pages to front the complete book: 'As sight and steadiness of hand begin to fail me I shall

22

Richard Mead FRCP. The son of a nonconformist minister, Mead was born in Stepney in 1673 and studied classics at Utrecht University before going on to the University of Leyden where he studied medicine. He then set up his medical practice in Stepney, but moved to the City when he was appointed physician of St Thomas' Hospital. He took his Oxford doctorate in 1707 and, having moved to Bloomsbury, he was elected FRCP in 1716. He built up a huge and lucrative practice, spending his money on his collections of manuscripts, books and natural objects. As a collector he almost rivalled Sir Hans Sloane. Mead was a very popular man who, in Dr Johnson's words, 'lived more in the broad sunshine of life than almost any man'. He died in 1754.

beg leave to inform such gentlemen who have formerly employed me in drawing or any other way that I shall for the future decline all such business.'[31] He was then 57 years old and entitled to doubt continuing dexterity. Time showed that the doubts were only in his mind for he was still drawing 13 years later with another 300 drawings and three more volumes published to add to his credits.

The completed book established Edwards as an ornithologist. The *Gentlemen's Magazine* called it 'a work...executed with great abilities as well as with respect to the accuracy and perspicuity of the descriptions as the beauty and elegance of its cuts'. The Royal Society awarded him the Copley Medal in 1750: this was a signal honour as the medal was usually given only for experimental work. John Harrison had received it the year before for his chronometer used to calculate longitude and, later, Benjamin Franklin gained the medal for his work on lightning conductors.

THE BLACK-FOOTED PENGUIN

From *A Natural History of Birds*, Part 2

'The Black-Footed Penguin' was so called to distinguish it from 'the Penguin' which Edwards has described earlier as having a red bill and feet. He depicts here the bill of both types of bird which, he adds '. . . fully proves them to be of two distinct species'.

Exactly where either species came from was something of a mystery to Edwards and indeed others. Of the black-footed penguins shown here, he writes: 'The first of these birds was lent to me by Mr Cowell (who was a surgeon in Lombard Street) and the other by Mr Holmes; they could not say directly whence they were brought, but, as they came by East India ships, I suppose they were from the Cape of Good Hope . . .' Of the habitat and appearance of the penguins described earlier, Edwards wrote:

> 'This bird was lent me by Mr Peter Colinson; he could not tell from whence it came. I find them mention'd chiefly by voyagers to the Straights of Magellan, and the Cape of Good Hope.
>
> In Sir Tho. Roe's *Voyage to India*, I find this account: "On the Isle of Penguin is a sort of fowl of that name, that goes upright; his wings without feathers, hanging down like sleeves, faced by white, they do not fly, but walk in parcels, keeping regularly their own quarters".
>
> The above-mentioned Penguin Isle is near the Cape of Good Hope. I have examin'd some of the Voyages to the Straights of Magellan, and find very little account of the penguins there, more than they go upright, and burrow under the shores: So that I cannot determine the above-describ'd to be a native of any certain part of the world. Had these voyages given flight descriptions of the things they mention, we might from thence probably have fixed its native place.'

Published December 1745 by Geo Edwards

94

25

THE WORLD OF COLLECTORS

Edwards' writings are now of more interest to the social historian than the ornithologist. In his prefaces and special sections he discoursed on his own life and views, the techniques of painting and etching, adding occasional news items. 'On the fourth day of August 1748', he wrote, 'vast numbers of the great brownish spotted locust settled in all parts of the City...which surprised the inhabitants as no such event was remembered to have happened before.'[32] Of greatest interest is the text that accompanies each illustration describing how and from whom he got the specimen. These comments throw much light on the socially varied world of 18th century collectors, the brotherhood of the curious.

The aviaries of aristocrats afforded Edwards the opportunity to draw from life. The Duke of Richmond had a large aviary at his Whitehall house, not to mention a celebrated menagerie at Goodwood. Lord Burlington had an aviary at his newly built Chiswick House, as did his neighbour, Lord Wilmington. The Duke of Montagu's aviary at Blackheath had demoiselle cranes and at Parsons Green Sir Charles Wager, First Lord of the Admiralty, kept many exotic birds, often obtained by the navy and sometimes traded to Sloane. Sir Hans Sloane had such live birds as an Arabian bustard and an American vulture, as well as a menagerie with animals like the porcupine and wolverine. His Egyptian cat, contented upon a velvet-covered stool in Edwards' picture, must have been a household pet.

Edwards was often involved with collectors whose prime interest was botany, fauna taking second place. At that time the collection and cultivation of rare plants was enthusiastically pursued and easier to achieve than the transport of live animals and birds from far away places (witness Sloane's safe transport of plants from Jamaica in 1688 and the fate of his three animals: his servant shot the snake; the giant lizard, frightened by the crew, jumped overboard; and the alligator just died). Mark Catesby collected more flora than fauna during his long stays in America (1710-19 and 1722-26). He was a real field naturalist, travelling far to find his specimens in their natural habitat. By contrast, Edwards was the stay-at-home, waiting for his specimens to arrive from foreign lands. Catesby's collecting was partly financed by Sloane, Peter Collinson and Lord Petre.

Collinson was a rich Quaker cloth merchant with business interests in

America, and botany was his first love. Lord Petre had all round brilliance and was a botanist of genius. The friendship between the Quaker merchant and the young Roman Catholic peer was so deep that they could discuss religion together without rancour.[33] Collinson wrote enthusiastically of the Great Stove, a hothouse of gigantic proportions that Petre built at Thorndon Park, near Brentwood; Edwards pictured one of the plants growing there. Tragically, Petre died in 1742 of smallpox when only 29 years old, leaving some 200,000 species of plants in cultivation at Thorndon Park.

Collinson, like Sloane, used Edwards to portray animals as well as birds, getting him to draw a sloth (preserved) in 1734.[34] Indeed Collinson was most generous with his specimens and Edwards wrote that he was 'on all occasions willing to oblige me with the use of every new subject he receives from foreign countries'.[35] Above all, Collinson was on good terms with all in the magic circle of the Royal Society and so a great help to Edwards in extending his acquaintance with collectors.

Collinson and Petre initiated a regular import of American plants collected for them by John Bartram, a Quaker farmer in Philadelphia who turned to botany. This connection was taken over and expanded by the Quaker physician John Fothergill.[33] Thanks to Collinson and Fothergill, Edwards was able to get a regular supply of American birds from the Bartram family, particularly John's third son, William, who became America's leading naturalist. Working in London, Edwards depended on the major British trade routes for his specimens. Canadian specimens were supplied by Alexander Light and James Isham, both of the Hudson Bay Company. Isham, who had been in charge of several trading posts, made his own collection of natural objects and artifacts from that region. Dr Massey, who catalogued the College of Physicians library before Edwards became bedell, had connections with the Company, from which he got a live eagle and a porcupine. The eagle he kept at his house in Stepney, the porcupine he gave to Sloane. Both specimens were portrayed by Edwards, who also depicted the red locust that Massey found in a basket of pineapples and fed with vine leaves.

The captains of the East India Company's fleet provided many specimens for collectors and were particularly useful to Edwards. Charles Dubois, the Company's secretary, used the ships to transport his specimens, which were drawn by Edwards and some of them given to Sloane. By similar means Dr Mead obtained 'a large cargo of natural rarities' that was examined by Edwards, who also described how Captain Worth of the Company introduced Chinese goldfish into England in 1728. One bright entrepreneur later bred them on the island of St Helena to shorten the voyage home. Rather grandly, the Duke of Richmond had a huge Chinese earthenware vessel made to carry his goldfish all the way from China.[36] Another enthusiast tried to ship back a live rhinoceros. It died during the voyage, but not before it was sketched by a passenger; Edwards made a picture from the sketch.

The Dutch sailors brought back specimens from the East Indies and from the little Dutch colony of Surinam in central America. This gave rise to a trade in dead exotic birds from Holland to England. Dr Mortimer used the trade to get East Indian birds, as did Richmond for his large collection of Surinamese birds. In fact birds from Surinam gained undue prominence in English collections thanks to the Dutch navigators. Sloane had many pictures of these birds drawn by the 17th century Dutch artist Anna-Maria Meriam when she visited Surinam.

Edwards always wanted to know where birds came from as it was 'very material to their natural history.' Dealers were often ignorant or untruthful on this important point. A green parrot he bought from a dealer was 'a brisk and nimble bird and talkative in a language unknown to me.' A melancholy cause of confusion was the slave trade. The captains of British slave ships would take African birds as gifts to the plantation owners in the West Indies. In turn the owners would despatch the birds as gifts to friends in England, using a slave ship returning home. Edwards was thus able to explain why several African birds had been wrongly labelled as natives of America.

Talking birds were very popular with all classes. Edwards pictured the mynah owned by Dr Wharton, treasurer of the College of Physicians, and wrote 'for whistling, singing and talking it is accounted in the first rank, expressing words into an accent nearer human than parrots.' Judging from the numbers of the parrot family that Edwards pictured, these birds were top of the popularity stakes. He bought them at Bartholomew Fair, at a shop called the Parrot and Cage, and from a publican in the Strand who had a sideline in exotic birds.

Stuffed birds were of necessity the staple of a collection. Edwards was either well versed in their preparation or knew the appropriate experts. Richmond wrote to him from Goodwood: 'I shall send you up in a day or two a small bird...which I desire you would draw and then prepare him with feathers so that I may put him in my collection.'[37] Stuffed birds were also used as decorations in coffee and ale houses. Edwards drew birds in Salter's Chelsea coffee house. These may have been cast-offs from Sloane's collection as Salter had once been his servant and advertised his establishment as the 'Museum Coffee House' or as the 'Chelsea

John Fothergill. Born in Wensleydale, Yorkshire in 1712, Fothergill was a lifelong Quaker and a very able physician. He took his MD in Edinburgh and in 1740 started to practice in London. He obtained his Licentiate of the Royal College of Physicians in 1744, the first Edinburgh graduate to be admitted. He built up the finest private garden in Europe at his estate in West Ham and had close contacts with many American scientists, being an early member of the American Philosophical Society, Philadelphia.

JOHN FOTHERGILL M.D. F.R.S.

Knackatory.' The house was known best for the strength of its punch and for Salter's ability to entertain with his violin or to pull teeth if required.[38] Sloane had a picture of a black and white diver, drawn by Sir Thomas Browne, physician and author of *Religio Medici*, but Edwards drew the bird from a specimen in the Marlborough Head ale house.

Edwards' searches for specimens illustrate how widely a love of collecting nature's oddities was spread through society. He drew a butcher bird from a cage full of them brought back from Denmark by Lady Albemarle, who in 1743 had gone to Copenhagen, escorting Princess Louisa for her betrothal to the Crown Prince of Denmark. Away from high society Edwards received a steady supply of birds from Catesby's brother in Gibraltar, who spent his time shooting anything flying. A London housewife gave birds supplied to her from Lisbon. He also pictured many birds collected by Mrs Kennon, midwife to the Princess of Wales, whose goldfinch 'stuffed and set upon a perch' was a prize possession. A City apothecary asked Edwards to draw the mongoose he kept to free the house of rats. A stag beetle from East India was brought to Edwards by his good friend Mr Pope, 'a gentleman well known for many curious and useful inventions, particularly for Marbling Paper with a margent to prevent fraud in publick offices'. First Albin and then Edwards were employed to figure the Indian birds collected by Joseph Dandridge. He was a Huguenot silk weaver with a considerable collection of natural objects, but remained in the tight circle of the Huguenot silk industry and outside the close-knit collectors of the Royal Society.

Of the physicians who encouraged Edwards, Dr Robert Nesbitt provided his collection of Chinese butterflies and Dr Matthew Lee his exotic beetles. Nesbitt served the College as a Censor for some years and Lee, who practised in Oxford before coming to London, was physician to the Prince of Wales. Dr James Munro, known for his excellent work with the insane at Bethlem Hospital, was the most expert ornithologist among the physicians. As a youth he started his study of birds on an expedition to St Kilda. He knew a lot about seasonal plumage changes and advised Edwards on the subject. He also tried, and failed, to breed Chinese pheasants at his home in Croydon. Sloane succeeded in breeding them, and the Duke of Leeds informed Edwards that his grandfather had bred them successfully but the birds 'were all destroyed by some disobliging neighbours'.

A love of natural history, especially of birds, was common among the upper and middle classes and transcended social barriers. Edwards mixed freely with all, and made friends of many. As the rich could afford the best collections, Edwards spent much time with the aristocracy. He was particularly popular with the ladies, from Sir Robert Walpole's wife and Lady Anson to Lady Wager, who took more interest in the aviary than did her husband, Sir Charles.

WORK WITH THE PHYSICIANS

While carving out a career as a naturalist, Edwards was a good and faithful servant to the College of Physicians. He was honest, above bribery and the peculations of minor office so prevalent at the time. As bedell he supervised the maintenance of the College's large building, from water supply to all repairs (surprisingly the plumber was a woman). He was responsible for all domestic purchases, from food and candles to brooms and chamber-pots. His neat itemised bills are still preserved in the archives.

He organised the meetings of fellows, both professional and social. In this he was helped by his artistic skills as he both designed and etched the plates for the various printed summons to the College and for the College Diploma. This saved the College some money as Edwards received only a small fee for each plate, far less than the College paid to other engravers after Edwards retired. The summons for fellows to attend Comitia required attendance *cum pileo et toga*, which sounds better than cap and gown. Dinners were held at three o'clock, 'please do not bring your servant, waiters will be provided.'

Each of the plates etched was decorated with the College's Coat of Arms. Edwards made at least three versions of the Arms, granted in 1546, adding a lot of rococo decoration around the shield on which the blazon was displayed. Notably, he added a Greek motto[39], taken from Hippocrates and usually translated as 'life is short, the art long.' The College had never had a motto, nor is there any evidence that it adopted one in Edwards' day. It would appear that the motto was entirely Edwards' idea, accepted by the College by later continuous use.

Edwards arranged the annual Croonian sermon, instituted in 1749 according to the 'will of the Lady Sadleir pursuant to the design of her first husband, William Croone MD FRS'. The first preacher was the Reverend Tom Birch, secretary of the Royal Society and a friend of Edwards, who collected the first six sermons into book form with the contents page set out in his own hand.[40]

The bedell was also concerned with administering College properties. In this he had the advice of James Mead, the attorney retained by the College, who lived within the College building and bought Edwards' books. The care of legal documents appears to have been the job of the

THE LITTLE GREEN PARROT
From *A Natural History of Birds*, Part 4

This was George Edwards' own parrot which he kept at the College. After a detailed description of the bird, which was 'about the size of a pigeon', he writes: 'I cannot be certain from what part of the world this bird was brought, it being out of dealer's hands, who could not inform me; though I take it to be from the West Indies, from whence most of the Green Parrots we have in London are brought. It was my property; I kept it alive for some years; it was a brisk, lively, nimble bird, and talkative in a language unknown to me. I have observed that Parrots have more or less briskness and agility in proportion to their size, the greater kind being very clumsy and slow in their motions, and the lesser more and more nimble, as they decrease in bigness. I don't know that this is any where described.'

bedell, as Edwards got excited on finding the great seal of Oliver Cromwell attached to a deed belonging to the College's Essex estate, given to it by Hamey.

More important, the bedell had to keep the list of fellows and licentiates, collecting fees and fines when appropriate. In doing so Edwards was involved in two interlocking and protracted disputes which showed up the College as a bastion of undue privilege. In 1747 Dr Isaac Schomberg, son of a successful physician who had been disciplined by the College, set up practice in London and then sought the College's licence to do so. Usually, this would have been granted but a squalid row followed. It was Edwards, not the president, who signed the order forbidding Schomberg to practise, and another order stopping any fellow from consulting with him. Eventually, the College had to abandon its untenable position and the Schombergs were vindicated. By that time many licentiates were accusing the College of depriving them of their rights. Things came to a head in 1752 when their grievances were set out in a memorial signed by several distinguished physicians, including Dr John Fothergill.

Meanwhile Edwards was sued by Dr Clephane and, in another writ, by seven licentiates for taking their licence fee and denying them their rights. It is remarkable that they sued the College's servant and not its president or treasurer. Once again the College climbed down and legal action was suspended.[41] During the dispute the College expunged the names of the dissenting licentiates from its official list. They retaliated by publishing their own list which Edwards duly obtained and filed with his own collection of College lists, marking it 'published by a discontented part of the licentiates'.[42] It must have been an unpleasant time for Edwards: it says much for the regard in which he was held that the Schombergs bought his books, as did Samuel Pyle, a licentiate who sued him. Dr Fothergill continued to be an enthusiastic supporter of Edwards' work on natural history.

The bedell's duty in the library was to ensure the safety of the books and the return of borrowed volumes. In charge of the library was the Harveian librarian, who had to be a fellow of the College, although the post was not always filled. Dr Richard Tyson was appointed Harveian librarian a year after Edwards became the bedell. Tyson's father, Dr Edward Tyson, was a physician best known for his account of the orangoutang, which turned out to be a chimpanzee.

Edwards must have influenced Tyson's choice of books for he bought several on natural history, including Willughby's book on fish, in which

Sr   *College of Physitians*

You are desir'd to Dine with the President, and Fellows, at the College, on Friday next, the 28 day of September 1744 at three of the clock in the afternoon precisely

                                  Your Most Humble Servt

                                  Geo Edwards

Dr Mead
Dr Tyson
Sr Edwd Hulse   } *Stewards*
Dr Jurin

This invitation to dine with the President and Fellows of the College (above) and the summons to Comitia (right) are examples of the domestic duties Edwards combined with his artistic endeavours in the service of the College.

Dominus Præses orat Excellentiam tuam, Dr Eximie, ut Comitijs Ordinarijs Majoribus intersis in Ædibus Collegij die Lunæ primo Mensis Octobris hora quinta præcise cum Pileo et Toga. Anno 1744.

                               A.V.B.

                               Geo Edwards

I was in Essex at this time.

THE GERBUA

From *Gleanings from Natural History*, Part 1

According to Edwards, gerbuas* were found in Egypt and the Barbary Coast, but this live specimen was the property of Mr Scarlet, an optician near St Ann's Church, Westminster.

Edwards described the gerbua as '. . . in general shape as near that of a rat except the nose and for legs are shorter and the hind legs much longer . . . . It is said to have one vent only, as in birds; but this I cannot affirm as I could not conveniently handle the living animal, which would bite when held fast.'

*'Gerbua' is the spelling used by Edwards; 'Jerboa' is the more modern spelling.

Cuniculus seu Lepus Indicus, Vrias dictus
of Aldrouans

The Gerbo of le Bruyn
in his Voyage to the Levant in english folio P. 287 Plate 210

219

This Animal is calld AL JERBUA, or JERBUA, and is figur'd & describ'd in Del Tesoro Britannico Delineate e Des=
critte da Nicola Francesco Haym Romano. Vol. 2.º pa. 124. 125. The living Animal (from which this was drawn
of its natural Size) is now the Property of Mr. Scarlett, Optician, by St. Anns Church, Westminster. Mr. Blen.
Librarian to the Inner Temple, had also lately one of them living: It is remarkable that it hops like a Bird.
on its hinder Legs, never setting its fore Paws on the Ground, but generally hides them in ye Furr under its Throat.

37

An etching of an elephant made by Edwards in 1752. He pasted this etching into an anatomical account of the elephant that had been accidentally burnt in Dublin in 1681. The account was published in 1682 and later presented by Edwards to the College library where it still remains.

Edwards inserted several of his own pictures. Edwards gave the library a 1682 account of an elephant's anatomy, adding his 1752 engraving of the beast, its legs shown like wrinkled stockings. Of course he gave to the library each of his own volumes as they were published, each beautifully bound. The College gave him five guineas for each; half-bound, they sold at two guineas.

Dr Tyson became president in 1746, but continued as Harveian Librarian until his death in 1750. After that Edwards received an extra £10 a year for his work in the library, for no Harveian Librarian was appointed. Surprisingly, the task of making a new catalogue of the library was not given to Edwards: he was probably pleased when he could remember the exact location of a book, requested by Tom Birch, that was omitted from the new catalogue. In telling Birch how to find it, he added 'If I am out of the way, I shall order my maid to attend you to the library.'[43] There was no doubt about who was in charge.

CHANGING TIMES

In 1754 Edwards was sufficiently well known to have his portrait paint-ed and engraved copies made. The engraving is of such wooden formal-ity that no character is revealed, it merely confirms Robson's description of a man 'inclined to corpulence.' Linnaeus hung a copy in his Uppsala study, where it reminded him of Edwards' 'indefatigable assiduity in collecting, delineating and describing'.[23] That is exactly what Edwards did and how he did it.

By now, death had deprived him of many of his early supporters. Mark Catesby died in 1748 and Edwards set about revising a second edition of the book on Carolina, publishing it in 1754. He kept a copy which he coloured to his own satisfaction. The second Duke of Richmond died in 1750 and Sir Hans Sloane died in 1753, followed a year later by Dr Mead and Folkes.

It was the death of Sloane that affected Edwards most deeply. He described how Sloane, confined by infirmity to his Chelsea manor, 'requested it as a favour to him...that I would visit him every week to divert him from an hour or two with the common news and any thing that should happen amongst his acquaintance at the Royal Society and other ingenious gentlemen many of whom I am weekly conversant with: and I seldom missed drinking coffee on a Saturday morning the whole time of his retirement in Chelsea.' Edwards' last visit was on the day of Sloane's death: 'I was greatly surprised to find so good a man in the agonies of death.'[44] He could not bear to see his old friend in such dis-tress and left before the end.

Time did not change the tempo of Edwards' work. He was still picking up gossip and knowledge as a regular guest of the Royal Society, where he made a series of presentations, mostly of animals and birds. However, he joined in the fashionable habit of commenting on natural phenomena. The Lisbon earthquake of November 1755 drew a shoal of letters to the Society, each with a different explanation of the disaster: Edwards, in a long letter, advanced the theory that a minute interrup-tion of the earth's rotation was the cause. In the same vein he wrote of a curious afterglow in the sky, starting 'On Sunday evening the 5th of June 1757, being walking in the fields near Islington...I observed...'[27] Many a country clergyman addressed the Society in this way.

Edwards was eventually elected a fellow of the Royal Society in November 1757. By then he had given ten formal presentations, four being published in the *Philosophical Transactions*. Collinson, Theobald and Baker again signed the proposal for election, as did Birch, Pond and da Costa. The Reverend Tom Birch, already a close friend of Edwards', was secretary of the Society from 1752 to his death in 1765. According to Dr Johnson, he was as witty in conversation as he was dull in his prose. Birch specialised in biography, often illustrated with portraits etched by Arthur Pond, who was an artist by profession. Mendes da Costa was a rogue, but an intelligent one. A notary turned naturalist, he specialised in fossils and started a book on them in 1751. The work was interrupted for three years when he was imprisoned for debt.[45] 'The world', wrote Edwards, 'was impatient for the book's completion.' The first, and only, part was published in 1757. The *Dictionary of National Biography* wrongly attributes a book on fossils to Edwards. Da Costa's career ended abruptly when he defrauded the Royal Society, but the good Dr Fothergill still befriended him.

THE LAST BOOKS

Whatever he had said at the time, Edwards' ambitions to publish were not extinguished when he completed 'Birds'. By the time he was admitted a fellow of the Royal Society his plans for another book were well advanced. As he wanted to show that he was a naturalist, rather than a pure ornithologist, he chose a new title, *Gleanings of Natural History*. However, he continued the numeration of the plates from 'Birds'. It was a shrewd business venture. His 'Birds', he wrote, had 'gone on smoothly without any competition...It has circulated in most parts of Europe.'[46] Both points were true. The French edition of the book had ensured its entry to Europe and in Germany his work, combined with that of Catesby, was published serially. To have a complete set of Edwards' pictures and descriptions, those who had subscribed to 'Birds' would have to buy 'Gleanings' and new subscribers to 'Gleanings' would have to purchase the four volumes of 'Birds'.

His excuse for further publication was the number of new 'curious objects' that he had depicted. In fact he made much use of his existing portfolio, particularly for pictures of quadrupeds, reptiles, fish and insects. Some of the etchings had been made long ago, notably one published in 1743 from a picture made in 1733. For the first time he had four etchings made by a professional from his original paintings.

New collectors were taking over from the old. John Bartram still sent specimens from America, but his young son William began to send drawings, which Edwards copied, and in 1756 sent a large parcel of birds, with written notes. Dr Fothergill, who supplied Edwards with many specimens, did a lot to encourage young William as a fellow Quaker, as he grew to be America's leading field naturalist. William and the ageing Edwards had much in common. Both were pushed into business by their fathers and hated it; William failed dismally as a manager of a general store. Both loved drawing from nature and both were well liked life-long bachelors.

Edwards' fame had spread enough for him to receive a Brazilian bird from Peter Tesdorf of Lubeck who had obtained it in Lisbon, a truly international exchange. Dr Alex Russell, FRCP and master of languages, sent birds from Aleppo where he practised for 15 years, returning to London to write up the natural history of the place. Dr Patrick Browne sent birds from Jamaica, and later wrote a natural history of the island to supersede Sloane's work. Gideon Loten, Governor of Ceylon, retired to London and allowed Edwards the use of his collections of birds and bird paintings.

London collectors still came from diverse backgrounds. Dr Chauncey, FRCP and bibliophile, supplied birds and went so far as to buy five copies of Edwards' books. Joseph Ames, a ships' chandler who studied the history of printing and became secretary of the Society of Antiquaries, sent for Edwards to draw the little owl that fell down his chimney. Edwards watched a live jerboa owned by the librarian of the Middle Temple, then drew one owned by a Westminster optician, picturing the animal hopping across the desert in front of the Pyramids. Other collectors included the MP for Hazlemere, Philip Webb FRS, a city druggist, a Whitehall bookseller and Mr Brooks of Holborn, 'a great dealer in foreign birds and curious poultry.'

Edwards did a lot of work on the collection owned by James Leman, which included the Ganges crocodiles once owned by Dr Mead and described by Edwards at the Royal Society. The intriguing thing about Leman was that Edwards always referred to him as being in or of the College of Physicians. The College archives show that Leman did live in a house within the College building, renting it from 1755 to 1760. His tenancy, as an outsider, was not unique: a London mercer had a similar lease before him. James Leman's father was, like Joseph Dandridge, a Huguenot silk weaver and amateur naturalist. The son was apprenticed as a weaver, but his later occupation is unknown.[47] What with Leman's live birds and Edwards' parrots and monkey, the College must have been as noisy as a zoo. Indeed the monkey, 'a very lively, diverting and good natured creature', had to go, finding a safe home with Lord Tylney at Wanstead.

Naturalists were confused at that time about large monkeys and small men. So Linnaeus in Sweden was excited when he heard that a troglodyte, *Homo nocturnus*, had turned up in London. He wrote, in February 1758, to John Ellis FRS, an Irish-born merchant and naturalist who discovered that corals were animals, not plants, asking him to find the troglodyte and requesting that 'the excellent Mr Edwards would make a drawing of this individual.' It is no surprise that Ellis failed to find it, but he went to the College where he 'examined in our friend Edwards' possession Dr Tyson's anatomy of the orang-outang' and the 'same kind of animal still preserved in the College of Physicians'.[23] Edwards later sent Linnaeus the skin of a chimpanzee from the College museum which also had a zebra skin, used by Edwards for his drawing

Carl Linnaeus (or Von Linné) 1707–1778. Linnaeus first studied medicine at Uppsala University, Sweden. From 1735–1738 he worked on botany in Holland and 1735 published Systema Naturae, the first of his many books classifying plants and animals. In 1736 he visited Sir Hans Sloane and others in England and in 1741 became Professor of Practical Medicine at Uppsala and developed an international liaison with other scientists. He retired in 1774 after suffering a stroke. In 1783 a young English physician, James Smith, bought all Linnaeus' library, manuscripts, archives and herbarium for 800 guineas. The Linnaean Society holds the collection.

of the animal. These two records provide the only evidence that the College had a museum collection in Edwards' time; presumably he looked after it. The original College building did house a museum containing specimens of natural history, carefully catalogued by Dr Christopher Merrett, naturalist of note. The collection, and the building, were destroyed by the Great Fire but Merrett's catalogue survived.[48]

Edwards' house in the College must have been a hive of activity. He was busy etching the plates for his new book, sending uncoloured prints to Linnaeus. He was also engaged in the laborious work of making new paintings, as substitutes for the etchings, to be bound with the text of his 'Birds' and 'Gleanings'. The volumes were given to Tom Birch in 1758. There could have been no higher mark of friendship and respect. These volumes (extended by Edwards to cover all of 'Gleanings') are now in the British Library and afford a unique comparison of Edwards' watercolours with his published etchings.[49] The uncoloured plates of 'Gleanings' sent to Linnaeus can now be seen at the Linnaean Society. To be certain of seeing Edwards' published work coloured by his own hand, the volumes in the Royal College of Physicians should be consulted.

43

THE POMPADOUR
From *Gleanings of Natural History*, Part 3

Edwards used his observations of the birds he depicted to attempt to put them into their correct taxonomic groupings. Of the Pompadour, which was a native of Cayana in South America, he writes: 'It is of a family of birds I have called Manakins. The nearest European bird that I know of that will class with this American tribe is the *Garrulus Bohemicus.* It agrees with them in the size, shape of the bill, and shortness of the tail . . . (and) in the tips of the first row of covert feathers.'

Of his name for the bird, Edwards writes: 'This is one of those birds taken in a French prize* by the now Right Honourable Earl Ferrers . . . They were said to be for Madam Pompadour. It being a bird of excessive beauty, I hope the Lady will forgive me for calling it by her name.'

*Captured ship

The Pondadore, drawn from nature of the size of Life, by George Edwards. May. 30. AD. 1759.

341

45

'Gleanings' was published from the Royal College of Physicians with the text in English and French (by the Reverend Duplessis) set side by side. The fact that Britain was then at war with France did not concern Edwards. He was confident that, as conflict did not interrupt intellectual communication between the two countries, the French would buy his book.

The first volume published in 1758 was dedicated to the Trustees of the newly opened British Museum which housed Sloane's huge collections and to which Edwards gave an important picture of the Dodo. He described his etching of the bird (in the second volume of 'Gleanings') as 'taken from a picture drawn in Holland from the living bird from St Maurice's Island in the early times of the discovery of the Indies by way of the Cape of Good Hope. It was the property of the late Hans Sloane to the time of his death: and afterwards becoming my property I deposited it in the British Museum.' That a Dodo survived the journey is wonder enough. That Sloane left such a rare picture to Edwards is proof of their friendship.

This oil painting of the Dodo was attributed in the Museum's gift book to the Dutch painter Roelandt Savery and dated 1627. It was much copied in the 19th century and is now in the possession of the Natural History Museum, although not on public display. Across the top of the painting is written 'The Dodo. Given by G Edwards FRS, AD 1759.'

In the second volume, published in 1760, Edwards announced that 'to convince the world that nothing further could be published by me, I must inform them that...all my original drawings are sold to a generous purchaser and are now the property of a Noble Earl.' True to form, Edwards continued to draw and etch, and published a further volume. The noble earl was Lord Bute, to whom Edwards dedicated the volume. Bute was a strange purchaser. As a keen knowledgable botanist he had no obvious interest in birds, had never commissioned a drawing by Edwards and had refused to join the Royal Society which provided Edwards with patrons. The reason for the purchase, which cost Bute £300, was that he wished to give the portfolio of some 900 pictures to the King. 'I apprehend' wrote Edwards in 1763 'that they are for the King's new Library now fitting up at Buckingham House.'[50] By that time George III had ended the intimate friendship with Bute that he had enjoyed as Prince of Wales. Alas, Edwards' portfolio is not in the Royal Collection, nor is there any evidence that Bute ever delivered his gift to the King.

The Dodo. From the painting in oils of a live bird brought to Holland. Attributed to the Dutch artist Roelandt Savery, 1627, the painting shows macaws, mallard, widgeon and heron. The picture was bequeathed by Sir Hans Sloane to George Edwards who gave it to the British Museum in 1759. The picture is now in the possession of the Natural History Museum. (Courtesy of the Natural History Museum.)

Horace Walpole was much amused by Edwards dedicating his book to Bute. In a letter to his friend George Montagu he wrote 'I was much diverted t'other morning with another volume of birds by Edwards...what struck me most were his dedications; the last to God; this to Lord Bute; as if he was determined to make his fortune in one world or t'other.'[51] It is an odd measure of Edwards' reputation that Walpole should include him in his high society gossip. Edwards was genuinely religious, seeing God through His Creation. He never sought patronage and it is unlikely that he considered Bute as a potentially helpful patron.

As Edwards had anticipated, 'Gleanings' capitalised the success of his 'Birds'. Some 500 copies went to subscribers, who included Horace Walpole, Benjamin Franklin, 38 physicians and people living in St Petersburgh, Danzig, Stockholm and Copenhagen, Pennsylvania and the Barbadoes. Copies were sent to the British Museum, the universities of Oxford and Cambridge, and the Academy of Science in Paris. Edwards donated his usual copy to the College of Physicians and to the Royal

Society. His reputation as a naturalist was advanced, and Linnaeus told him that his 'representations' were so accurate that 'nothing is wanting to the birds but their song'.[23]

With such a compliment and the general approbation of naturalists it was a little churlish of Edwards to complain, in the second part of 'Gleanings', that 'several of our manufacturers that imitate China ware, several print sellers and printers of linen and cotton cloths have filled the shops in London with images, pictures and prints copied...after the figures in my history of birds'.[52] Far from being flattered, Edwards was annoyed by his imitators, though he gave no reason for his annoyance. He was not so naive as to expect a cash recompense from the imitators and, as he thought the imitations were poor, it is unlikely that he would have wished his name to be linked with the designs. Probably he was put out to find his scientific work trivialised for the sake of decoration. However, if his claim was true, Edwards was the unwitting source of a fashion in decoration that grew more popular after his death.

Certainly the Chelsea pottery made porcelain birds modelled directly from Edwards' illustrations. The porcelain had the raised anchor mark discontinued in 1752 and the birds modelled were taken from Edwards' first two volumes. It was Dr Bellamy Gardner[53] who first identified the figures in 1931, a total of 16 birds. At the same time he showed that 10 embossed bird paintings had been copied from Edwards' work by Samuel Dixon, a Dublin painter and print seller who also had a shop in London.

Although not relevant to Edwards' complaint about the china making industry, it has been shown recently that the Sèvres tea service (and some other Sevres pieces) at Goodwood House are decorated with exact copies of Edwards' pictures. The porcelain was made at the Sèvres factory in the mid-1760s by order of the third Duke of Richmond: he may well have sent the factory Edwards' presentation volumes given to the second Duke.[54]

Printed textiles, mostly of cloth made from cotton and linen,[55] stem from 1750 when the calico industry introduced printing from copperplates. This technique was exploited from 1765 onwards with intricate designs of birds and flowers. However, Barbara Morris failed to find any direct representations of Edwards' birds on textile patterns.[56]

It would appear that Edwards was exaggerating the profusion of imitations because bird patterns decorating porcelain and textiles did not become really fashionable until after 1765. Yet he may well have had a considerable influence on the designers' work as they would have been familiar with Edwards' pictures. Of course, Edwards did have a tendency to think that any picture of a bird must have been an imitation of his own work.

Mr William Drummond has drawn attention to the work of Samuel Northcote, an obscure artist, who in 1768 painted two watercolours of birds that are accurate copies of Edwards' published plates. One is of the coot-footed tringa, the other of the painted pheasant from China, inscribed '... Sir Hans Sloane kept this bird which is a cock about 15 years.' The text is derived from Edwards' but neither picture indicates in any way that it is a copy. No doubt there were examples of copyists that made Edwards wince.

THE BEDELL RESIGNS

True to form, Edwards had used the 1760 sale of his portfolio 'to convince the world that nothing further can be published by me',[57] and continued to draw as before. But age was beginning to tell. In August 1760 he apologised to his friends for being a tardy correspondent: 'but they must excuse the slowness of old age, because it is an infirmity of nature'.[23] At the same time he resigned his office of bedell to the College of Physicians in the summer of 1760.

The new bedell, Edmond Barker, was appointed immediately, without fuss or ballot. Edwards bought himself a small house in Plaistow, and he looked set to retire to the rural delights of his youth. Given his character, it is no surprise to find that he continued to work at, and for, the College of Physicians. The list of parliamentary electors for December 1762 records Edwards as a freeholder of Plaistow but gives his abode as Warwick Lane. In October of that year Edwards wrote from Plaistow to tell Tom Birch that he had completed 'a set of 51 coloured prints designed for a 3rd part of *Gleanings of Natural History*.' So much for convincing the world that he could never publish again. His letter, with his inimitable spelling, expressed his desire to have the prints approved by the Royal Society so that his work 'may be distinguished from some late published volluminous Natural Historys which have no vouchers for their autensity but their authors...My Privet obligations to many gentlemen of the Royal Society as well as my Gratitude for the public honour I have received from the Society as an incorperated boddy will alwais ingage me in their service.'[43]

It is not clear as to who was being attacked by Edwards, but he disliked any rivalry, however diffident his manner was said to be. Maybe his target was Thomas Tennant who started publishing his *British Zoology* in 1761. Edwards wrote of Tennant as 'a gentleman of Flintshire of a large fortune and great personal merit', omitting any comment on his skill as a naturalist. Tennant, in his autobiography, thought that Edwards was initially jealous of him, but was later of help: 'He presented me...with numbers of his original drawings...These I have kept...as a curious testimony of his faithful and elegant pencil.'[58] Tennant indeed was using his fortune to publish a work that depended on others, as he was no artist and not a great naturalist. Edwards also knew the rival French

Ornithologia by Jacques Brisson, published in 1760, and he had criticised the quality of the illustrations; Brisson may have been the target of Edwards' letter.

The story behind the last volume of 'Gleanings' lies in its dedication to the Earl of Ferrers FRS, who succeeded to the title held by his bad-tempered brother, publicly executed in 1760 for the murder of his steward. The book, wrote Edwards, had 'almost received its being from a most curious parcel of Natural Objects...which fortunately fell into your Lordship's hands during the late war'.[59] Lord Ferrers, then Captain Shirley Washington RN, had taken a French prize homeward bound from South America. The 'parcel' on board was a collection of exotic birds, a gift for La Pompadour. Edwards was sorry that 'any beautiful lady should be disappointed in so reasonable amusement; tho' I am overjoyed to see the prize in London'. He named one of the birds 'Pompadour', 'it being a bird of excessive beauty, I hope that the Lady will forgive me for calling it by her name'.[60]

The book also included illustrations of specimens from Bartram and Fothergill, and some collected by Edwards on a summer holiday in the Isle of Wight and on a winter visit to Yarmouth. One old etching was dated 1753 and the etched titles of two new plates had a personal note: 'drawn on the Coronation Day of George and Charlotte, Sept. 22nd 1761' and 'drawn by Geo. Edwards in the 70th year of his life.' Age had not impaired his skill. The book ended with a list, with Edwards' own classification, of all the objects depicted in the seven volumes of his work. Some 500 objects were recorded on 310 plates. The text, once again, was in English and French but this time the French text was by Edmond Barker, the new bedell to the College of Physicians. This collaboration suggests that Edwards had a hand in the appointment of his successor.

The book was published from the College of Physicians in 1764. It was Edwards' last work, but he continued to give unofficial help with the administration of the College. He finally returned his collection of College lists in May 1767, stating in an accompanying letter that 'the whole of my service and residence in the College were the years 1733 to 1766', and bidding farewell to the fellows as 'their late domestic and still very much obliged servant'.[42] 'Residence' needs qualifying, for Edwards' will of 1770 shows that he then owned chambers in Clifford's Inn, Fleet Street. He may have bought them in 1766 on his complete retirement from the College, but it is more likely that the purchase was made when he had to relinquish the bedell's house in the College in 1760. Barker and Edwards are unlikely to have shared living quarters, however much of Edwards' work was done in the bedell's house.

THE SMALL AMERICAN REDSTART

From *A Natural History of Birds*, Part 2

In describing the position in which he chose to depict this bird, Edwards writes: 'The sides, and all the covert feathers within side of the wings, are of a bright orange-colour, which being one of his greatest beauties, I have given him an action on purpose to shew it'.

The manner in which Edwards used the work of Mark Catesby as a source of information while perceiving him as a rival is well illustrated by the following passage:

> 'Mr Cromwell, surgeon, in Lombard-Street, obliged me with a sight of this bird; he received it from Jamaica, with some others. I found in Sir Hans Sloane's *History of Jamaica* a description of this bird, but no figure . . . Mr Catesby in his *Natural History of Carolina* has mentioned it also . . . where you will find a figure of it. He says, "These birds frequent the shady wood of Virginia, and are seen only in summer, and that the hens are brown". He calls it the Redstart, whose example I have taken, as I think the name very proper. Sir Hans Sloane has given it no English name. Seeing it a bird of passage in Virginia, I suppose it may be so too in Jamaica, which may be perhaps its winter habitation; but of this I have received no account. This plate was finished, and the colouring far advanced, before I recollected the bird to be in Mr. Catesby's works; otherwise I should have omitted it: But I hope it will not be altogether lost labour, since there are many encouragers of this work who have not been purchasers of Mr. Catesby's *Natural History*.'

Mr Peter Collinson (city merchant and a botanist) had given Edwards the butterfly in the figure, which had been brought from Montserrat in the West Indies.

It had been a long, busy and successful combination of two careers. After the greatness of Sloane, Edwards served eight easily forgotten presidents of the College; for more than 20 years the College employed a bedell who was more distinguished than any of its presidents.

Robson, admittedly writing about a dead friend whose work he was trying to sell, called Edwards a man 'of liberal disposition and cheerful conversation' and, for those who shared his interests, 'a most entertaining as well as communicative companion'.[5] Edwards' social life revolved round learned societies and his good friends were collectors from many walks of life. However, Robson added that his diffidence and humility were always apparent. They were apparent in his initial refusal to become an FRS, but not in the daemon that drove his work. He poured out pictures, sure that his was the hand of authentic description. Yet, repeatedly, he announced that it was all too much for him and that he would retire. His temperament was manic-depressive. Critical of any work that he thought imitated or rivalled his, he wrote of how time would bring his work to oblivion and that, after his death, his pictures might 'be come by at easy rates as things that have served their turn'. Like others of his time, he viewed nature from the town and had no interest in the countryside or its guardians, the hunting squires, whom he considered stupid and saw no point in educating their sons as it did not need knowledge for them to break their necks out hunting.[61]

Despite his wide acquaintanceships, Edwards was a private person, singularly devoid of worldly ambition. His twin careers came late in life and were arranged by others. He never sought preferment in the venal competitive society of the 18th century. As a young man he defied his father's wish that he should become a merchant: the defiance may well have proved easy by his father's death. During the long years in his parents' home his only close companions were his two sisters and, as he showed on his journeys, he was content with his own company. He never married and lived for years in the exclusively male environment of the College of Physicians.

A possible clue to Edwards' complex personality is to be found in his diatribe against single sex education that he wrote in his second volume of 'Gleanings'. It is the only passage in the book that Horace Walpole pounced upon. 'Edwards', wrote Walpole, 'proposes that all schools of boys and girls should be promiscuous, lest if separated they should learn wayward passions'.[51] Edwards meant more than that. He introduced the subject by noting that his bantam cocks, when kept apart from hens, would tread each other, an example, he said, of how natural appetites might be deviated into wrong channels. With considerable

George Edwards FRS, *portrayed in his seventieth year, three years after he retired as bedell to the Royal College of Physicians.*

force he continued with his condemnation of schools which kept boys away from girls when their 'natural affections were blossoming' and so 'acts unnatural' were introduced in place of the natural. Edwards went on to emphasise that as the unnatural acts were criminal offences, a bachelor could easily fall prey to blackmail.[62] This suggests that Edwards was himself a homosexual and had experienced the threat of blackmail. There is also the mystery of the young Lawrence Gray to whom Edwards, in his will of 1770, bequeathed his chambers in Clifford's Inn, to be held by his executor until Lawrence reached his majority. The bequest was cancelled by a codicil of 1772 which stated that Lawrence had bought the chambers from Edwards. It was the only bequest that Edwards made to anyone outside his family.

55

HUMMING BIRD, WAXWING, BULL & GOLD FINCH, GREAT TIT, ROBIN AND OTHER BIRDS AND BUTTERFLIES

Untitled painting 12 x 20¼ inches. Signed and dated 'Edwards 1732'
Photograph, courtesy Mr William Drummond

THE LAST YEARS

The last years at Plaistow were all downhill. Edwards lost the sight of one eye and suffered much from a stone in the bladder. In 1769 he sold to Robson, the bookseller and his biographer, 'all the remaining copies of my natural history in seven volumes...together with all my copper-plates, letterpress and every article in my possession relative to it'.[63] He announced the sale from the College of Physicians, which presumably had continued to house all these items.

He was not quite done with life, managing to travel to a few cities and to write a last letter to the Royal Society in 1772 on why the English climate was milder than that of America on the same latitude. He was also making a 'Garden of Agriculture' at his Plaistow home. His planting was delayed because the Chelsea Physic Garden (run by the College of Physicians) failed to deliver the seeds.[64] The writing of Edwards' letter of complaint was spidery with age.

His end came slowly and painfully. He died on 23 July 1773 at the age of 80 years. He was buried in West Ham and his tombstone (long since disappeared) recorded him as 'Formerly Librarian to the Royal College of Physicians, in which Capacity he was universally and deservedly esteemed. His Natural History of Birds will remain a lasting monument of his knowledge and ingenuity'.[65]

The sole executrix of his will[66] was Ann Edwards, his spinster sister. To her he left 'all my Real Estates at West Ham and Plaistow'. The West Ham property must have been his parents' house, and Ann was probably still living in it. To Ann he also bequeathed £60 a year and to his married sister, Mary Tracy, £30 a year, being the interest on £3000 invested in 3% stock. The capital sum was to pass, on the death of his sisters, to the three children of his late half-brother, James Frost. Ten guineas went to a first cousin. All went to the family apart from the bequest to Lawrence Gray, already noted (p 55): this bequest was cancelled by the codicil of 1772 that noted the death of the cousin and recorded a remarkable increase in the investment in 3% stock to £5000, accruing in two years of retirement. In all, it was a significant estate, gained, in Robson's words, 'by assiduous application to his favourite pursuits'; a neat financial epitaph.

A year later Robson sold Edwards' library, 'the property of a man of distinction.' In 1776 Robson published his own biographical memoir on Edwards together with a reprint of Edwards' contributions to the *Philosophical Transactions* of the Royal Society and a list compiled by Linnaeus of the Latin names of all the species described by Edwards. Sir Joseph Banks, who had collected some of Edwards' watercolours,[67] found the printing of the list inaccurate, writing on his copy: 'I compared the foregoing list with Linnaeus' original letter to Mr Robson and made the alterations which appear on it.'

Robson's biography was reprinted, without acknowledgement, in the *Universal Magazine* and used by Nicholls for his 'Literary Anecdotes'. Robson told Nicholls that he had written the biography for two reasons: 'the first is but a piece of vanity, that my name will be enrolled amongst the Worthies of the age; and the next, it may recommend the sale of the works of my deceased friend'.[68] Edwards' work was inevitably eclipsed by a surge of new knowledge that led to many books on ornithology, illustrated by fine artists. Yet his work has never drifted into the oblivion that he foresaw. As it is some 220 years since Robson's memoir was published, it seems a reasonable time to produce a new biography of George Edwards, particularly one written from the Royal College of Physicians which he served so well and for so long.

EDWARDS ON COLOUR
From *A Natural History of Birds*, Part 4

Throughout his books, George Edwards described his techniques for drawing, etching and colouring. In the following extract, he gives his views on how to colour:

'. . . In speaking of colours, I shall not perplex the reader, as the common books on the subject of drawing, etc. have done; which tell you what to mix together for a ship, trees, the earth, a brick house, lyon, fox, etc. for these particulars are trifling and superflous. The way to colour well is, when we are provided with all necessary colours, to consult the natural colours of the objects we would represent; then by casting the eye over the colours we have ready prepared, it is very likely we may find something that in many cases will serve our turn, pure and unmixed; but if we cannot, let us consider the colours in a compound sense. We have an object, for example, which is purple; amongst our colours we do not find that, but by mixing red and blue it is produced. Blue and yellow, produce green. Red and yellow, make an orange-colour. Red, blue and yellow, makes browns, and cloth colours of all kinds, by varying the quantities of each; so that red, blue and yellow, by a compound of some two of them, produce the fine colours, viz. purple, green, and orange-colour; and the three primary colours, red, blue and yellow, compounded all together, in different proportions, produce all the different degrees of browns and cloth-colours, and a shadow for white itself: For if you take a round piece of card-paper, and divide it into three parts, by lines from the center to the circumference, and wash these three parts with the three primary colours, so that neither of them be too strong for the other, and all of them pretty light, then fix a pin in the center, and turn it about swiftly, you will find the colours will be lost in each other, and the paper will appear white, thought not so pure a white as before it was coloured.'

EDWARDS' WORDS

If George Edwards is remembered it is as a pioneer bird artist of merit. This is as he would have wished, but his writings are well worth reading for his felicity with words. Scattered through his books are gems of vivid description and much that tells of his personality. He wrote with firm conviction of his love of God and His creation, on accuracy of observation and recording, of learning and justice. The flavour of his style is shown in the following short extracts from his book.

On nature

'Every one ought to attain to as high a degree of natural knowledge as he can, for a deep knowledge in nature has detected many false pretenders to inspiration, prophesy, and the like, while the ignorant in nature and her laws have been deluded by the meanest pretenders, such as diabolical possessions, fanatical apparitions, dreams, good and bad, omens, and the like.'

From the Preface to *A Natural History of Birds*, Part 1

On drawing

'Natural history cannot in any degree be perfect without figures; therefore I think we should promote drawing, in all such young people who seem to have a liking to it; no one need think it an amusement beneath his dignity, since our present Royal Family and many of the young nobility have been instructed in that art. The world may perhaps think I say this in order to promote my self; because hitherto I have taught young gentlemen and ladies to draw; but to take away such imputation, I purpose to decline any thing of that sort which may hereafter offer.'

From the Preface to *A Natural History of Birds*, Part 1

On preserving a specimen

The Black and White King-Fisher '...This bird was preserv'd in spirits, with many others, in a glass to bring to England; the white part appeared very dirty and yellow, which, I believe, was owing only to its being stained with the foul spirits; for I have observ'd such changes in feathers which I knew otherwise to be purely white.

N.B. If any one would draw a bird preserv'd in spirits, let him take it out, wash it pretty well in warm water, and rinse it in a good quantity of cold, and let it dry gradually, and he will restore the true colour of the feathers, as far as can be; for some feathers in the glasses of spirits, I have observed to appear of colours very contrary to the true colour they are of before they were put in.'

From *A Natural History of Birds*, Part 1

On plumage

The Cock Padda or Rice-Bird '...Tho' this bird has but little gay colouring in it, yet is it a bird of much beauty, the feathers all over, except the wings, appear to have a fine soft bloom on them, like that on plumbs, and fall on one another in such order that no feather can be distinguished, but the whole appears with a surface smooth and even. I saw one of these birds alive at Sir Hans Sloane's: they came from China.'

From *A Natural History of Birds*, Part 1

The White-Belly'd Humming Bird '...the colours in this bird, as in most of this kind, seem to be mixed golden threads, which make the whole bird appear very splendid, when exposed to the sun-beams.'

From *A Natural History of Birds*, Part 1

The Long-Tail'd Green Humming Bird '...It hath a very long and broad tail, in proportion to the body, the feathers being very firm and stiff, not easily put in disorder; the bill is slender, straight, pretty long, and of a black colour; the crown of the head is blue, or else the bird is mostly green; the quills are of a dirty purplish colour, except three green ones next the body; the coverts of the wings are green; the lower belly, and coverts under the tail, are white, the thighs dusky; the tail-feathers are of the most shining beauty that can be imagined, appearing sometimes of a shining blue-colour, and upon a little turn will change greenish, then again into a colour mixed with a bright golden splendor; the feathers, all over the body have something of a shining golden lustre, but nothing in comparison with the beauty of the tail; the legs, feet, and claws, are black.

This bird was brought from Jamaica by Capt. Chandler at Stepney, of whom I procur'd leave to take a drawing of it.'

From *A Natural History of Birds*, Part 1

On light

'Colours require a certain degree of light to shew them in their greatest perfection, and make them appear their proper distinctions one from another: for, as the light declines to darkness, all colours are lost in the sable hue: and, if light be increased to the highest degree, by bringing the sun's rays to a point through a convex glass, and that light be thrown on bodies of various colours, they will all appear the same, the excess of light wholly overcoming the colours. Vid.'

From the Preface to *A Natural History of Birds*, Part 2

On migration

'It is indeed my opinion, that all those birds which are seen with us only some part of the year, pass into other countries when they are out of our sight. We are certain some of them must, because they do not breed while they continue with us: these are the wood-cock, snipes, field-fare, redwing and some others: These I believe, go into northern countries to breed. The summer birds of passage also come from more southern countries northward to us, and breed here: seeing then birds retire from more northern parts to winter with us, why should not tender birds who visit us in summer and breed here, retire and shelter themselves in southern countries, where they are secure from cold, which they cannot bear, and such food as is natural to them. But many would make sleepers of them and say they retire to holes under ground, and in hollow trees, etc. and that they are so fat that they cannot fly far at the times they disappear, which fatness I take rather for a providential provision, to enable them to take a flight of many days without being quite exhausted and spent. A farther reason to me, that our summer birds who disappear are not sleepers, is, that no such sleeping birds have at any time been found, and all the reports of these things are so uncertain, that no sober man can at all depend on them: Did they really creep into holes as is reported, it would be certainly known, and not remain as it does, a very doubtful matter; for why should they not be daily found sleeping, as are dormice, by wood-men and country people, since many of the supposed sleepers are found awake in much greater numbers. I believe indeed that the instinct of these birds is not so absolutely certain, as to prevent them from being sometimes surprised by a very cold wet autumn: In such a case I believe some flocks of swallows have lost their passage, and have been constrain'd through weakness to shelter themselves in holes where they have perished.'

From the Preface to *A Natural History of Birds*, Part 1

On nocturnal and diurnal animals

'Amongst animals there are, in respect to their sight and time of action, diurnal, nocturnal, and such as act in the morning and evening twilight. Amongst the first may be placed men and monkeys, from the *Homo Silvestris* down to the smallest species of monkeys properly so called. Not long since I had a little monkey of St. Jago, of the same species with that figured plate 215 of this work, who was so very nimble, that, when he got loose in a small room, I could not catch him; but, on shutting the light out of the room, I could take him presently. Birds of the granivorous kind are, I believe, all diurnal: and birds of prey are divided into diurnal and nocturnal; though many of those esteemed diurnal will prey in the evening and morning twilight, as most of the eagle and hawk kind do. Owls cannot bear the day, and do not fly till the twilight advances towards night; but whether or not they fly in dark nights, I cannot tell. I believe many of the water-fowls to be nocturnal; for herns, bitterns, and some others, are seen on the wing in the morning and evening twilight. Many of the quadrupeds see both in the night and in the day, but the cat kind more remarkably; for they not only range and prey in the night, but delight also to bask in the hot sunshine at noonday, though their eyes are not formed to bear so strong a light; but nature has given them a power to contract the pupil of the eye in such a manner, that no more light is admitted that what their eyes can bear. The bat is wholly a nocturnal quadruped, never appearing by day. All sorts of cattle that graze in the fields are diurnal, and, in some measure, nocturnal; for they move about and feed in the night. Beasts of prey are, in a stricter sense, nocturnal, because the night is their principal time of seeking their prey; nevertheless, most of them, occasionally appear and ravage in the day time.'

From the Preface to *A Natural History of Birds*, Part 2

Asides and observations

The Whip-Poor-Will, or lesser Goat-Sucker '...Mr Mark Catesby obliged me with this bird; it was brought from Virginia, and there was another brought with it, which compared in all its marks, but more obscure, which I suppose to be the female

To illustrate this history, I shall add a quotation from a letter Mr. Catesby received with these birds from a gentleman in America.

"They come to Virginia about the middle of April, from which time, till the end of June, they are heard every night, beginning about dusk, and continuing till break of day; but it is chiefly in the upper or western parts that they are so frequent; I never heard but one in the maritime parts; but near the mountains in the month of May, within a few minutes after sun set, they begin, and make so very loud and shrill a noise all night, which the echoes from the mountains increase to such a degree, that the first time I lodged there I could hardly sleep: They are seldom seen in the day-time. The Indians imagine these birds are the souls of their ancestors formerly slaughtered by the English, and say, that they never appeared in their country before the slaughter. Many people here look on them as birds of ill-omen. I have been informed they lay two eggs of a dark green, spotted and scrolled with black, in the plain beaten paths, without any sign of a nest, upon which they sit very close, and will suffer a near approach before they fly off."

From *A Natural History of Birds*, Part 2

The Grey Finch, the Wax Bill and the Caterpillar '...The Caterpillar, added by way of decoration, at the bottom of the plate, is of a dirty-brownish yellow colour; it is drawn of its natural bigness; its rings and shape are best described by the figure. What is most extraordinary in it is, that the four rows of knobs which rise like the heads of small brass nails, of a yellow mataline-colour, are of such transcendent lustre and brightness, as not to be in any sort of imitated by art; for in my opinion, they excel polished goal, in the same degree that gold excels brass. It is preserved in spirits, and is in the Museum of Richard Mead, M.D. Physician in Ordinary to the King, who obliged me with the use of it. It was etched on the copper immediately from nature.'

From *A Natural History of Birds*, Part 4

The Indian Ichneumon [Mongoose] '...This animal seemed to me to be of the size of a ferret, or pole-cat: It was about three quarters of a yard, or twenty-seven inches long; the tail from a thick base ended in a point like that of a lizard.

It had a pretty sharp nose, covered with short hairs of a reddish-brown colour; the eyes were bright and sparkling, like a ferret's, . . .

I saw this curious animal at Mr. Bradbury's apothecary, in South-ampton Buildings, Holborn, whither I was directed to go to draw it, by Dr. Wilmot, Physician in Ordinary to his Majesty. Mr. Bradbury was so very obliging, as to order it to be catched, and brought into a small room, where I might observe all its actions. Sometimes it crept with its belly to the ground, and stretched itself out so long that it seemed to resemble a serpent moving without feet; at other times it raised its head, and appeared to walk on its legs, shortening its body a little; it would also sit very upright on its hinder legs, and look about it, and then anger'd would set up its bristles in a surprising manner.'

From *A Natural History of Birds*, Part 4

The Little Indian Buffalo '...I saw one of these buffalo's, kept some time grazing in the Artillery-Ground, London, and observing a picture after nature of the same animal, which agreed exactly with it, in the house of Sir Hans Sloane, at Chelsea, I contented myself with engraving a plate from the picture, for I could not have made a better from nature. Sir

Hans told me his picture was an original from nature, done by order of the late Sir Josiah Child, of Wanstead in Essex, Bart. The creature was a present to Sir Josiah, from the East-Indies. The picture was afterwards given to Sir Hans Sloane, by Mrs. Cassandra Willughby, afterwards Dutchess of Chandois. It is one of their domestick cattle in India. I have often hear Sir Hans Sloane say, that of the shin-bones of this buffalo burnt, or half calcined, are made what in the East-Indies are commonly called serpentine stones, being pretended to be taken out of the heads of the serpents, called Cobras de Cabelo; to which they attribute a wonderful property of extracting the poison, if applied to the wound, and that being washed in milk and dried, they are again fit for use.'

From *A Natural History of Birds*, Part 4

The African Land-Tortoise '...I had the male and female of this species; they lived two years with me, in the garden of the College of Physicians, London.'

From *A Natural History of Birds*, Part 4

NOTES AND REFERENCES

(References to George Edwards' own writings in *A Natural History of Uncommon Birds and in Gleanings of Natural History* are abbreviated to 'Birds' and 'Gleanings' respectively. Roman numerals have been used to denote the parts of the books.)

1. This account of the formation and early years of the Royal Society is based on Dorothy Stimsom, 1949, *Scientists and Amateurs*. Sigma Books, London.

2. Recorded by Hamey's nephew, Ralph Palmer, in his MS *Life of the most eminent Dr Baldwin Hamey*. MS in Library of Royal College of Physicians.

3. The bookplate's heraldic significance was kindly researched by Mr CJ Holyoake, using the copy in the Library, Royal College of Physicians.

4. 'Birds' II, 121-4.

5. J Robson, 1776. *Some memoirs of the life and work of George Edwards*.

6. 'Gleanings' II, III.

7. The pictures that Edwards made for Hans Sloane are in the British Library, Manuscript Department, Add. MS 5263, 5264, 5267, 5271, 5272, and in the British Museum, Print Department, C203 Vol I.

8. 'Gleanings' III, Preface.

9. 'Birds' I, XIX.

10. 'Birds' II, 119.

11. Bedell is derived from the Latin *Bedellus*, used in the original statutes of the Royal College of Physicians. In Edwards' time the College used the term Beadle but for the last 150 years the College has constantly used Bedell.

12. 'Birds' II, IV.

13. See LM Payne and CE Newman, 1970. *J.Roy.Coll.Physns.Lond.* 4, 234. The College's acquisition of the Dorchester Library is an involved and exciting story. The books were finally housed in the College in 1687, in a library converted from the candidates' room on the advice of Sir Christopher Wren. The Dorchester collection is still the prized possession of the College.

14. 'Birds' IV, 182.

15. 'Birds' I, XVII.

16. The print, together with some other uncoloured prints by Edwards, is bound into Seymer's copy of 'Gleanings'. The book is held by the Linnaean Society, London.

17. 'Gleanings' III, II.18. 'Gleanings' III.

19. 'Gleanings' III, III.

20. For a full appraisal of Edwards' etchings, compared with other artists, see Christine Jackson, 1985. *Bird Etchings*. Cornell University Press.

21. Vol I of 'Birds' published in 1743 contained six plates published in 1741 and seven published in 1742. Vol II published in 1747 had three plates published in 1743, 14 published in 1745 and seven published in 1746.

22. 'Gleanings' II, 276.

23. Letter published by JE Smith, 1821. *Correspondence of Linnaeus and other naturalists.*

24. That the menagerie at Goodwood was well stocked is evident from a letter written by the Duke to Sloane who had arranged for an unnamed agent to deliver a live sloth to the Duke. '...I wish indeed that it had been the sloth that had been sent me for that is the most curious animal I know; but this is nothing but a common young black bear which I do not know what to do with, for I have five of them already. ...I beg you would tell him not to send me any Bears, Eagles, Leopards or Tygers for I am overstocked with them already.' (British Library, Sloane MS 4078. f.66).

25. At the College of Physicians on 25 June 1728 Sir Hans Sloane, presi-

dent, told the 25 fellows assembled for Comitia (the formal quarterly meeting of the College) that "His Grace the Duke of Richmond was desirous of being admitted a fellow of the College having been made a doctor of physic upon His Majesty's late going to Cambridge'. Needless to say, the Duke was forthwith elected a fellow of the College. Sloane was not only a great friend of the Duke through their mutual interests in natural history and the Royal Society, but also the medical adviser to the Duke and all his family. Moreover, the two were related by marriage. The Duchess of Richmond was the daughter of Lord Cadogan whose younger brother married Sloane's daughter and later succeeded to his brother's title.

26. The original proposal is in the archives of the Royal Society.

27. The manuscript account of this presentation, together with all the MS letters and descriptions written by Edwards to the Royal Society, are in the archives of the Society.

28. This anecdote is quoted by Joan Evans, 1956. *History of the Society of Antiquaries*. Oxford Univ. Press.

29. Edwards' book, like others published in parts, was sold half-bound. The style of full binding was decided by the buyer to suit his library. Hence some copies of Edwards' book were bound into two volumes, each containing two parts of the book. Most copies have each volume bound separately.

30. 'Birds' III, advertisement (unpaged).

31. 'Birds' I, in added final title pages.

32. 'Birds' IV, 208.

33. See Hilda Grieve, 1981. *A Transatlantic Gardening Friendship*. Historical Association.

34. See the collected letters of Peter Collinson edited by A Armstrong (in press).

35. 'Gleanings' II, 166.

36. 'Birds' IV, 209.

37. Letter quoted by Edwards, 'Birds' IV, 228.

38. See B Lillywhite, 1963. *London Coffee Houses*. Allen & Unwin.

39. The Greek motto is printed in Roman letters.

40. The book of sermons is in the library of the College of Physicians.

41. For a full account of the Schomberg and the licentiates' controversy, see Sir George Clark, 1966. *A History of the Royal College of Physicians*, Vol II. Clarendon Press, Oxford.

42. Edwards' personal collection of College lists covering all his years as bedell is in the library of the College of Physicians.

43. Edwards' letters to Birch are in the British Library, MS Dept. (Add. MS 4305 and 4443). He also wrote to Birch about the Privy Seal of Oliver Cromwell, 'at present in my keeping. The Seal was attached to a deed of the Baldwin Hamey estate given to the College.'

44. 'Gleanings' II, III.

45. Peter Ascanius, a Danish zoologist, in a letter from London to Linnaeus, wrote: 'Da Costa is a Jew who has long laboured at a history of fossils in English. He certainly possesses an excellent collection of minerals; or rather, I should say, he did possess it for at present he is in prison for debt.' (see Ref.23).

46. 'Gleanings' II, I.

47. For the story of James Leman, father and son, see P. Thornton and M. Rothstein, 1958. *Proc.Huguenot Soc.* XX, 60.

48. Dr Merrett's catalogue is in the library of the College of Physicians.

49. The British Library shelf marks for Edwards' volumes presented to Birch are C.45. K8 and 9.

50. Letter, dated London May 7,1763, from George Edwards to Lord Cardross, recently acquired by the Royal College of Physicians. The full text reads:-

> My Lord I have received your Lordships Letter dat. Glasgow Feb.7.1763 and deferd returning an answer til I Had finished the 3rd part of my Gleanings, that I might send them together, this will be the Last thing I shall Ever Publish, for my materials are gone; they are bought by the Earl of Bute, they

amount to upward of 900 Original finished drawings and Sketches from life and I aprehend they are for the Kings new Liberary now fitting up at Buckingham House. You will find with your Book a few black Prints belonging to the part deliverd which I desire your Lordship to accept, and as I know that your Lordship has a good hand at colouring they may serve as an Amusement and with a little pains and high colouring they may appear like Drawings as I have experienced by some few I have coloured for framing which deceive Ordinary Judges. I am well pleas to hear that your Lordship designs to honour the Royal Society by becoming a Member of their body, I hope shortly Your Lordship will visit London that your friends may have the pleasure of your agreeable conversation, Mr Baker is well and joyns with me in compliments and respects to you and your Lordships noble family, I rest My Lord your Lordships most Humble and Obliged Servant Geo Edwards

P.S. the Earl of Bute Generously Payd me the Price I asked for my Drawings which was £300:0:0. Party divisions run high amongst us which hurts friends, conversation and the persutes of Drawing and Arts.

That Edwards' portfolio never came to the Royal Collection was kindly confirmed by the Hon Mrs Jane Roberts, Curator of the Print Room. After Bute's death his natural history pictures were sold in 1793. The sale catalogue (in the British Library) lists many pictures by 'Edwards'. Most of these are of flowers, often arranged in baskets, typical of the work of John Edwards, an artist flourishing around 1770–85. Some of the pictures of birds may well have been by George Edwards but would represent only a fraction of his portfolio. It is probable that the portfolio remained with the Bute family as Nicholls (see Ref. 68) referred to it in 1814, suggesting that 'the present Marquis would confer a favour on the public by causing engravings to be made from them as they contain a great number of English as well as foreign birds and other animals not accurately described or delineated.' A recent search of the Bute archives failed to reveal any evidence of the portfolio's continued existence.

51. WS Lewis (ed.), 1941. *Horace Walpole's Correspondence*, Vol 9. Yale University Press.

52. 'Gleanings' II, XXX.53. H Bellamy Gardner, 1931. *Brit.Porcelain Circle Trans. III*, 64.

54. The identification of Edwards' pictures copied on the Sèvres porcelain was made by Miss Gheniette Zelleke of the Art Institute of Chicago. Her work on French porcelain at Goodwood House is being prepared for publication.

55. From 1720 to 1774 it was illegal to sell in England pure cotton cloth with printed designs. The thriving calico industry got round this ban by printing on a cloth with a linen warp and a cotton weft.

56. Barbara Morris, 1957. *Antiques* LXXI, 556.

57. 'Gleanings' II, VII.

58. Quoted by Christine Jackson in *Bird Etchings* (see Ref. 20).

59. 'Gleanings' III, in Dedication (unpaged).

60. 'Gleanings' III, 224.

61. 'Gleanings' II, XXXIII.

62. 'Gleanings' II, XXI.

63. Edwards' announcement is recorded in *Notes and Queries* (1911) 4, 190.

64. The letter is in the library of the National Botanical Garden, Dublin.

65. Inscription recorded in *Essex Naturalist* (1903) XIII, 343.

66. Edwards' will is in the Public Records Office (PROB 11/990).

67. The watercolours are in the Banks Collection, Print Department, British Museum (194-D4).

68. J Nicholls, 1812. *Literary Anecdotes of the 18th Century*.